# PATTERNS OF SKIN pH
# FROM BIRTH THROUGH ADOLESCENCE
## With a Synopsis on Skin Growth

# PATTERNS OF SKIN pH
# FROM BIRTH
# THROUGH ADOLESCENCE

## With a Synopsis on Skin Growth

*By*

**HANS BEHRENDT, M.D. and MARVIN GREEN, M.D.**

*Department of Pediatrics*
*New York Medical College*
*New York, New York*

**CHARLES C THOMAS • PUBLISHER**

*Springfield • Illinois • U.S.A.*

*Published and Distributed Throughout the World by*

CHARLES C THOMAS • PUBLISHER

BANNERSTONE HOUSE

301-327 East Lawrence Avenue, Springfield, Illinois, U.S.A.

NATCHEZ PLANTATION HOUSE

735 North Atlantic Boulevard, Fort Lauderdale, Florida, U.S.A.

*With* THOMAS BOOKS *careful attention is given to all details of manufacturing and design. It is the Publisher's desire to present books that are satisfactory as to their physical qualities and artistic possibilities and appropriate for their particular use.* THOMAS BOOKS *will be true to those laws of quality that assure a good name and good will.*

*Printed in the United States of America*

*GG-11*

# FOREWORD

Regulation of surface pH is one of the important facets of skin function, being intimately related to the defense mechanisms of the skin. Changes in skin pH with age and maturation are indicative of developmental changes in skin function. Thus the seemingly esoteric subject of this monograph should be of concern to all students of developmental physiology.

As pediatricians, we have come to realize, somewhat tardily, that the established role of abnormal skin function in the pathogenesis of some systemic diseases may elude comprehension unless studied in the light of fetal and postnatal development of the integument. This growing concern is reflected by a steadily increasing number of pediatric contributions dealing with structure and function of the young child's sweating apparatus.

Our own interest in skin pH and skin function dates back to 1948, when age-dependent changes in axillary skin acidity were first revealed in a dermatologic study conducted by Dr. Franz Herrmann at the Skin and Cancer Unit of New York Post-Graduate Hospital, a study in which one of us (H.B.) was invited to participate. As a consequence of these findings, an investigation into the developmental aspects of skin pH was initiated jointly by the present authors.

It was not anticipated at the time that such an endeavor was bound to lead to our preoccupation with skin pH testing for many years to come. For the required large series of infants, children, and adolescents, subjects had to be procured from every available source, from private practice, clinics, wards, nursing homes as well as State Training Schools outside of New York City. We look with fond remembrance on our sojourning in the spring and autumn of rural New York, testing the pH on armpits of adolescents by appointment. Even today, measurement of surface pH is frequently performed in our clinical investigations. Altogether, we have tested over 1800 subjects.

Most of our findings have been published periodically; some have not yet been reported. We welcomed the invitation by the publisher to prepare a treatise on the developmental patterns of skin pH, in which we would expound our own work and pertinent contributions by others. It appeared indispensable for such a presentation to include an introductory outline of the morphologic and chemical changes in the skin associated with prenatal and postnatal growth.

In preparing the manuscript we were mindful of the variety of prospective readers, notably physiologists, dermatologists, and pediatricians, and their diversified interests. However, we did not allow such considerations to let us extend the scope of the discussion beyond the limits dictated by the factor of competence (or incompetence).

Our thanks are due to Dr. Franz Herrmann, who gave generous advice during the various stages of our investigational work. We also are indebted to the late Dr. Stephen Rothman, whose classic volume on biochemistry and physiology of the skin afforded invaluable help in the acquisition of knowledge and greatly facilitated the search for source material. We are most grateful to Mr. Bernard Carol for his counsel and assistance in handling the statistic evaluation of many of our published data. Finally, we are pleased to acknowledge the support we received from Dome Chemicals Inc. and from Johnson and Johnson Clinical Research Department at various phases of our studies.

New York, N. Y.                                                   H. BEHRENDT
                                                                  M. GREEN

# CONTENTS

# PATTERNS OF SKIN pH
# FROM BIRTH THROUGH ADOLESCENCE
## With a Synopsis on Skin Growth

# Chapter I

# DEVELOPMENTAL CHANGES IN STRUCTURE AND CHEMISTRY OF THE SKIN

## SKIN GROWTH AND BODY GROWTH

Participation of the skin organ in developmental changes of body composition is manifested by age-dependent alterations in the proportion of water to solid matter and in the concentration of extracellular and intracellular constituents. As most pertinent to the subject of skin pH we will review some data on skin hydration as well as on mineral and fat composition in relation to growth.

### Skin Water

The skin, in spite of its high affinity for water, participates in the steady decrease of body water which takes place between birth and maturity. Data on these changes found in the older European literature and recent measurements by Widdowson (156) are summarized in Table 1. The following correlations are indicated: The proportion of body water accounted for by total water in skin (freed from subcutaneous fat) increases during the second half of fetal life, but decreases strikingly from birth to adulthood. Extracellular water in skin represents a distinctly lower percentage of total skin water during the perinatal period than during the preceding fetal and the subsequent postnatal growth. However, there is a steady rise of the "fiber water" fraction of the extracellular skin fluid throughout fetal and postnatal development, while the reverse is true for the extracellular "nonfiber water." Widdowson considers fiber water to represent collagen water, and nonfiber water to derive from nonfibrous connective tissue proteins.

The intracellular component of skin water is lowest during fetal life, markedly higher throughout childhood and mature life, but exceedingly high during the neonatal period when extracellular skin fluid is much reduced. In neonates intracellular water in skin amounts to one tenth of total intracellular body fluid, as compared to 1.3% in the adult. Extracellular skin water represents one seventh of the extracellular body water in the neonate, and one fifth in the adult. The partition of skin water at different ages is illustrated in Figure 1.

Essentially, the same trend of changes has been found by Martner *et al.* (88) and by Metcoff (91), although their figures differ from those of Widdowson, especially with regard to the ratio of skin to body weight. Of interest also,

TABLE 1
DISTRIBUTION OF SKIN AND BODY WATER AT DIFFERENT STAGES OF
DEVELOPMENT*

|  | Fetus 20 Weeks | Full-term Neonates | Infants, 3-6 mos. | Adults |
|---|---|---|---|---|
| Skin weight as % body weight | 10 | 11 |  | 6 |
| Total body water as % body wight | 88 | 70 |  | 60 |
| Extracellular body water as % body weight as % total body water | 64 73 | 40 57 |  | 18 30 |
| Intracellular body water as % body weight as % total body water | 24 27.3 | 30 43 |  | 42 70 |
| Total skin water as % body water as % skin weight | 10.3 90.1 | 13 82.8 | 67.5 | 7 69.4 |
| Extracellular skin water as % total skin water as % total body water as % extracell. body water | 93.1 9.6 13.2 | 66.7 8.6 15.0 | 89.7 | 86.8 6.1 20.3 |
| Intracellular skin water as % total skin water as % total body water as % intracell. body water | 6.9 0.7 2.6 | 33.3 4.3 10.0 | 10.3 | 13.2 0.9 1.3 |

*Quoted or calculated from the tabulations of Widdowson and Dickerson (157) and Widdowson (156)

are the measurements of Metcoff on newborn premature infants, showing a tremendous increase in both intracellular and extracellular skin water.

During early life, intracellular fluid participates in changes of skin hydration to a greater extent than in later age. The two main sites concerned with the dynamics of skin water in older children and adults belong to the extracellular space (65) ; they are 1) the connective tissue of the cutis and 2) the base of the stratum corneum (see p. 28).

## Inorganic Constituents of Skin

Exceeding the earlier evidence in scope and accuracy, the work of Widdowson and Dickerson (157) has provided reliable information on the effect of growth on the skin's mineral content. As shown in Table 2, sodium and chloride contents (as well as water) decline during fetal development; sodium and water further decrease after birth, while chloride remains close to 70 mEq/L throughout postnatal life. Potassium content increases during fetal life and continues to rise during infancy, but is reduced subsequently; the value for adults is only half of that for 3- to 6-month-old infants. A similar reduction takes place in the phosphorous content between infancy and adulthood.

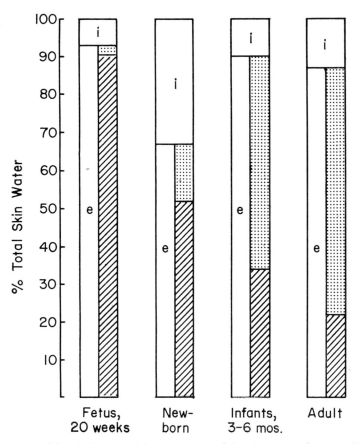

FIGURE 1. Water partition in human skin at 4 stages of development: *i*, intracellular water; *e*, extracellular water; *dotted areas,* fiber water; *lined areas,* nonfiber water. Drawn from data of Table 1 and additional findings by Widdowson (156).

TABLE 2
CHEMICAL COMPOSITION OF SKIN AT DIFFERENT STAGES OF
DEVELOPMENT*

| Constituent | Fetus | | Newborn Infant | Infants 3-6 Months | Adults |
|---|---|---|---|---|---|
| | 13-14 Weeks | 20-22 Weeks | | | |
| Water, gm | 917 | 901 | 828 | 675 | 694 |
| Total N, gm | 11.6 | 1.9 | 26.5 | 54.5 | 53.0 |
| Collagen N, gm | | 2.4 | 16.8 | 39.2 | 45.7 |
| Na, mEq | | 120 | 87.1 | 69.4 | 79.3 |
| K, mEq | 23.8 | 36.0 | 45.0 | 43.7 | 23.7 |
| Cl, mEq | 90.6 | 96.0 | 66.9 | 72.3 | 71.4 |
| P, mM | 41.8 | 28.2 | 31.7 | 34.9 | 14.0 |
| Mg, mEq | | 3.8 | 4.7 | 7.4 | 3.1 |
| Ca, mEq | 4.4 | 6.1 | 10.0 | 11.4 | 9.5 |

*Average concentrations per kg of fresh, fat-free skin (epidermis + corium).
From Widdowson and Dickerson (157).

Calcium appears to increase only during fetal life. Assertions (20,97) that calcium rises with age during postnatal life apply, if at all, only to sexually mature subjects. As Table 2 shows, the skin of the newborn infant has the same calcium content as that of older infants and the average adult.

## Nitrogenous Substances of Skin

Of particular interest is the marked rise of nitrogen derived from collagen during fetal growth and infancy (Table 2). This increase parallels the steady enlargement of the extracellular fiber-water space. Collagen nitrogen accounts for the major proportion of total nitrogen in the skin from infancy cross linkages. In globular proteins, the polypeptide chains are coiled or folded in close sets, often being of almost spherical shape.

Collagen and keratin represent the most important fibrous proteins in the skin; they must be distinguished from the globular proteins of plasma and most cells. According to Rothman (116g), the polypeptide chains of fibrous proteins are elongated and held in more or less parallel alignment by various cross linkages; collagen and keratin differ by the type and number of these cross linkages. In globular proteins, the polypeptide chains are coiled or folded in close sets, often being of almost spherical shape.

## Lipid Constituents of Skin

Like other tissues, skin contains "textural fats" which are part of the cellular structure and consist largely of sterols and phospholipids. In adults, fractional and total concentrations of these fats vary in a narrow range, as judged from the few analyses which can be considered as accurate. It has long been asserted, however, that the amount of structural lipids in epidermis and dermis declines with advancing development, fetal and postnatal. The early findings of Meyer (92) on the total cholesterol content of the skin are commonly quoted as evidence: 1203 mg/100 gm dry substrate in the fetus, 647 mg in neonates, 493 mg in children up to 14 years, and 367 mg in subjects over 14 years. Concentrations of free and total cholesterol are maintained at a ratio of about 4.5 through all stages of development. More phospholipids are present in cell-rich epidermis than in the corium. Similarly, analyses of hair fat for cholesterol (45,100) show that values for children are three times higher than for adults.

Skin tissue also contains fat which is deposited between cellular elements and resembles in composition the fat deposits in other tissues, particularly the subcutaneous fat. It consists largely of the glycerides of palmitic, stearic, and oleic acids. At any postnatal age, the amount of depot fat is greatly influenced by the nutritional state of the individual. In the adult, subcutaneous lipids contain 0.2% cholesterol, while 19.6% are found in skin lipids (45).

In most neonates, formation of the adult type of fat tissue is not yet complete, as indicated by the presence of varying amounts of embryonic fat cells arranged in round isles and containing almost no fat droplets. Only in a few instances, well-differentiated fat tissue is predominant, fully filled with fat as in adults. The firmness of such tissues increases with the amount of co-herent fat deposits. Since, histologically, the fat organ is considered to be a reticuloendothelial organ, and since isles of blood-forming tissue are occa-sionally found in the subcutaneous fat tissue (where capillaries approach sweat gland coils), it has been stated (7) that in the neonatal fat organ the processes of blood formation and fat storage are still in competition. The least-differentiated fat tissue of the neonate is that of the planta. There is little concise data on the age at which fat tissue development of the skin is complete in all regions of the body surface.

Comparative analyses carried out 60 to 70 years ago with methods avail-able at that time, already indicated the characteristic changes in composition of fat tissue with advancing age: an increase of the proportion of oleic acid to total fatty acids (triglycerides) from 43% in the newborn infant to 65% in 1-year-old children and to 90% in the adult. During the first twelve months of life the average iodine number rises from 43.4 to 62.4 (7).

Essentially, the same results were obtained in more recent studies carried out with modern analytic methods, as exemplified by the data of Table 3. As compared to the adult, the newborn full-term infant has twice as much pal-mitic acid (16:0), but only one third the amount of oleic acid (18:1), and one tenth of linoleic acid (18:2).

From Hirsch's recent treatise (69) we learn how these differences come about. Early in pregnancy, the composition of fetal fat deposits suggests that

TABLE 3
FATTY ACID PATTERNS IN HUMAN ADIPOSE TISSUE IN RELATION TO AGE

| Composite Fatty Acids[1] | Full Size Infants | | Young Adults[4] |
|---|---|---|---|
| | within 48 hrs. after Birth[2] | within 2 wks. after Birth[3] | |
| | as % of total fatty acid | | |
| 14:0 | 3.0 | 3.4 | 0.1 |
| 16:0 | 40.2 | 45.1 | 19.5 |
| 16:1 | 14.6 | 15.3 | 6.9 |
| 18:0 | 5.1 | 3.0 | 4.2 |
| 18:1 | 25.2 | 29.8 | 41.2 |
| 18:2 | 1.3 | 2.3 | 11.4 |
| 18:3 | 1.8 | .... | 0.4 |
| 20:3 | 3.9 | .... | 0.2 |
| 20:4 | 0.3 | .... | 0.2 |

[1]number of carbon atoms: number of double bonds.
[2]From Hirsch (70), average for 3 subjects.
[3]From Sweeney (139), average for 10 subjects.
[4]From Hirsch (69), average for 12 subjects.

they are derived from maternal lipids. However, as pregnancy progresses, fetal lipogenesis from carbohydrates becomes increasingly important; fatty acids thus formed and built into fats, are quite different from those derived from the maternal lipids (reflecting the pattern of food fat). While the fetal pattern of fatty acid composition is still found in the newborn infant, it is not maintained for long. Within several months after birth, depot fats take on a pattern resembling that of the ingested lipids.

> The nonsaturated fatty acids to be found in skin lipids of adults consist almost exclusively of compounds of the $\triangle^6$ series, which are not present in detectable amounts in other tissues. The sole exception is oleic acid, a compound of the $\triangle^9$ series to which almost all monounsaturated acids of the general metabolic pool belong. Nicolaides and Ray (99) have found that, as in adults, skin lipids of the neonate contain only unsaturated fatty acids of $\triangle^6$ series and concluded that these acids are synthesized *de novo* in the fetal skin. On the other hand, the results obtained by Downing and Green (41) indicate that the $\triangle^9$-unsaturated series constitute a major portion of the positional isomers in all chain-lengths of the neonatal lipids, except for[14]C and [16]C. The presence of both series suggests that the unsaturated fatty acids of fetal skin lipids have a dual origin, the $\triangle^6$ series being synthesized by the skin, the $\triangle^9$ series coming from the general metabolic pool and being incorporated per se.

Among the uncertainties of skin analysis for lipids is the problem of "sampling." By which rationale can lipid composition of skin tissue be equated with the lipid patterns found in hair fat obtained from barber shop sweepings (155), or in the surface matter removed from the scalp (98), or in the fetal material of vernix caseosa?

## EPIDERMIS

### Structure

Figure 2 illustrates how epidermal differentiation into five strata is attained. Developing from a single layer of ectodermal, nucleated, polygonal cells, the epidermis becomes two-layered at a fetal age variously given as 1, 2, or 3 months (7,126). The elements of the outer layer, or peridermis, show flattening and loss of nuclei; the inner or basal layer represents the rudimentary stratum germinativum with distinctly prismatic and elongated cells. There seems to be general agreement "that this germinative layer is the parent tissue of all subsequent cutaneous structures" (126).

At the fetal age of 3 to 4 months, the germinative cells begin to proliferate centrifugally to form the intermediate layer, subjacent to the peridermis; somewhat later, they also proliferate centripetally into the dermis, forming clusters of cells from which eventually the eccrine sweat glands and the pilosebaceous complexes develop.

Next, the intermediate layer undergoes stratification: its elements turn oval and smaller than the subjacent basal cells. Gradually, the stratum intermedium becomes the stratum spinosum. From about the fifth fetal month onwards, two new strata emerge from the outer layer of the spinosal stratum: the stratum granulosum, and the stratum corneum; the latter forms from cells ascending closer to the epidermal surface.

Concurrently with the development of the two new layers, the peridermis is being gradually shed and replaced by the stratum corneum. The manner in which cornification proceeds is described below.

With the eighth fetal month, differentiation into four distinct strata of characteristic histologic appearance is almost complete: the basal monolayer of germinative cells, the stratum spinosum (also referred to as "prickle layer" or "Malpighian layer") *, the stratum granulosum, and the stratum corneum.

At the time of birth, the basal stratum germinativum still shows structural irregularity, with neighboring cells not yet arranged in a continuing row, but dispersed in different directions; their shape is still round or polygonal rather than cylindric. The borderline between this basal stratum and the subjacent papillary structures of the corium (dermal-epidermal junction) can be defined only by special staining techniques at this age (7). The stratum spinosum contains cells "heaped into several irregular layers, dispersed in mosaic form" (126). Tonofibrils within the cytoplasm and intercellular bridges are already clearly discernible. The stratum granulosum consists of a thin layer of cells, not all of which contain yet the characteristic keratohyalin granules. The pink, relatively transparent appearance of the neonate's skin is in part attributable to this imperfect development of the stratum granulosum.

On palms and soles, the epidermis of the neonate reveals an additional layer, the stratum lucidum, which has developed above the stratum granulosum during the last fetal month. It has several parallel layers of flattened, nonnucleated cells, containing eleidin. As a multilayered stratum, the lucid-

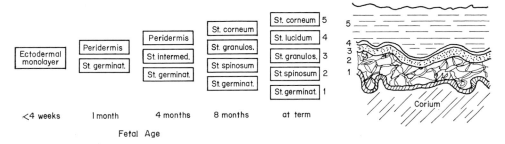

FIGURE 2. Epidermal strata at various stages of fetal development.

* If used correctly, as in the monographs of Kuno (77) and Montagna (94a), the term *stratum Malpighi* applies to the living portion of the human epidermis, comprising both the germinative and spinous layer. However, in the majority of American and European publications, especially in recent review articles (7,117,126), the stratum spinosum alone is referred to as the Malpighian layer.

um remains largely restricted to the friction areas of the skin, but can be found as a thin, one- to two-cell-deep layer in all human epidermis (94a).

The stratum corneum of the newborn infant is still thin; its cells are loosely arranged, some still nucleated; the most superficial elements are fused into residues of the vernix caseosa. This lack of coherence remains characteristic for the distal part of the horny layer known as stratum disjunctum cornei, while the lower part soon becomes compact and coherent (117). The base of this compact part, together with the subjacent stratum lucidum represent the "transitional layer" between cornified and noncornified epidermis, known as "barrier zone" or "barrier membrane." This thin layer functions as the main epidermal barrier against penetration of particulate substances from the ouside and as regulator of the transport of water and ions from the subjacent living cells through the cornified layers of the epidermis. The component most essential for these functions is a lipid-protein complex.

Progress toward full epidermal maturation is poorly defined. Development is probably not completed before the second month after birth, while subsequent changes are largely due to increase in mass. The time table outlined for the successive stages of epidermal differentiation represents a rough approximation, since the development is "dischronous in the various regions of the body" (126). Some authors (61) found the epidermal layers of 17- to 22-week-old human embryos to be as fully differentiated as in adult skin, though still containing glycogen deposits.

## Epidermal Keratinization

As pertinent to the chemistry of the skin surface, some important points of present concepts of epidermal keratinization should be stressed here. As characterized by Montagna (95), the epidermis is a unique biologic system in which growth and differentiation occur linearly. The mission of every epidermal cell is to reproduce, to prevent depletion, and to synthesize proteinous-lipid products. "Every cell begins to prepare to die as soon as it starts its journey to the surface, by synthesizing various proteinous products which we generally lump together as keratin."

According to Rothberg (114,115), the process begins at the basal layer "where cells closest to the dermal nutrient source obtain, integrate, and synthesize chemical components which form the DNA necessary for cellular reduplication." Rothberg conceives of one half of the mother cell as retaining its attachment to the dermis, the other half (or daughter half) as assuming responsibilities of keratinization. The cell remaining in the basal layer initiates nuclear processes required for reduplicating, while the daughter concerns itself with cytoplasmic processes that lead to synthesis of the protein or proteins forming transfilaments (114).

The first layers of emerging daughter cells comprise the stratum spinosum;

they show tonofibrils aggregated concentrically around the nucleus. Pushed further up the epidermis, the cells form the granular layer, showing further decomposition and keratinization; the nuclear membrane begins to disappear and synthesis of proteins continues. At the next level, the stratum lucidum and stratum conjunctum, the nuclei disappear and a lipid is formed. Both the granular and lucidum layer contain keratohyalin granules and eleidin droplets; their origin and nature remain largely undefined. Keratohyalin granules are known to contain calcium, but lack sulfhydryl or disulfide groups (94c), an indication that they play no direct role in keratinization. Finally, as the cells approach the surface, their life terminates with the formation of dead horny cells, with complete disintegration of nucleus and cytoplasm. As Montagna (95) puts it, the cornified cells, although dead, are capable of performing specific functions, mechanically and physiologically.

As one of the most impressive illustrations of epidermal structure, we have inserted a photomicrograph taken from Montagna's monograph (Fig. 3). It shows the fibrils, packed within each cell, to be oriented perpendicular to the skin surface in the proximal strata, but parellel to the surface in the distal strata.

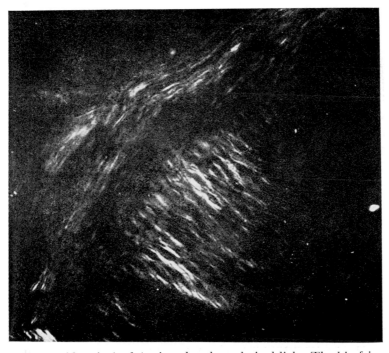

FIGURE 3. Human epidermis (scalp) viewed under polarized light. The birefringent fibrils from the basal layer to the granular layer are oriented perpendicular to the surface of the skin; above this point they are oriented parallel to the surface (top). From Montagna (94). (Reproduced with permission of the author and Academic Press.)

As compared to cell proteins, keratin proteins are characterized by their higher cystine content; the presence of disulfide cross linkages is believed to be the paramount chemical feature of the keratinization process (116h). Keratin proteins are synthesized *de novo* from amino acids at different levels of the epidermis, i.e., there is no preliminary formation in one layer followed by additional incorporation of cystine at a higher level (38).

## Chemical Composition

Water in molecular form can seep through the cylindrical interstices of the horny layer cells. The surface of these cells has been shown to be surrounded by a lipid layer consisting of cholesterol and fatty acids (138). When these lipids are removed by suitable solvents, gaps appear in the horny layer and facilitate penetration of water (144). Under normal conditions, the water content of the stratum corneum of the adult skin does not fall below 10% (137).

Considering the continuous liberation of amino acids from disintegrating cells and their utilization for keratin formation, it is not surprising to find relatively large amounts of amino acids among the epidermal constituents and in the seepage reaching the surface.

Other water-soluble components of the epidermal tissue which are apt to penetrate to the skin surface and to become constituents of the film cover include polypeptides, purine derivatives, and inorganic substances (see Table 6).

Conforming to the rule that cellular phospholipid content increases with the rate of proliferation and the number of mitochondria, phospholipids account for 2.62% of dry weight of the basal epidermal layer, but for only 0.14% of the horny layer (76). In fact, no phospholipids are found in the superficial nonviable cell layer; they apparently have disintegrated with increasing keratinization and do not reach the skin surface with other descendents of epidermal tissue.

Data on cholesterol content of the skin and its decline with advancing age have already been discussed and apply to both epidermis and dermis.

## Thickness of Epidermal Layers

Measurements reported in the European literature many decades ago and assembled by Becker (7) in 1954 are listed in Table 4. Although most of these determinations were made on untreated necropsy specimens by frozen section and are admittedly not very accurate, they may convey an idea of the general order of thickness and its great variability in different subjects of identical age and on different skin areas of the same individual.

Much lower values were obtained when fixed biopsy specimens were ex-

TABLE 4
DATA ON SKIN THICKNESS IN INFANTS AND ADULTS*

| | Epidermis mm | Stratum Corneum mm | Corium mm | Papillary Column mm |
|---|---|---|---|---|
| Newborn infant | 0.15–0.25 | | 0.7 –0.9 | |
| arm, flexor surface | | 0.01–0.1 | | 0.02 |
| abdomen | | 0.05–0.06 | 0.4 –0.7 | |
| back | | 0.01 | 1.0 –1.1 | |
| foot, palm | | 0.08–0.14 | | 0.09–0.12 |
| Infant, 9 months | | | | |
| back | | 0.01 | | |
| foot, palm | | 0.20 | | |
| Adult | | | | |
| average for all sites | | | 0.3 –2.4 | |
| average for all sites | | | 1.5 –2.0 | |
| average for all sites | | | 0.3 –4.0 | |
| cheek | 0.09–0.12 | | | |
| arm and leg | 0.07–0.1 | | | |
| hand and foot, palm | 0.5 –0.6 | | | |
| 2. finger pad | 0.8 –0.9 | | | 0.05–0.5 |
| back | | | 2.0 –3.0 | |

*Selected data from Becker (7).

amined (7): the thickness of the horny layers, for instance, ranged from 0.007 to 0.04 mm in the 1- to 10-day-old infants. It is questionable which mode of measurement yields results closest to the actual thickness. The stratum lucidum of the average adult is $5\mu$ to $10\mu$ thick (117), and consists of lamellae, each $0.5\mu$ to $2\mu$ thick.

Stuart and Sobel (135) measured shadows of skin plus subcutaneous tissue in roentgenograms of the calf in relation to age and sex in childhood.

## DERMIS (CORIUM)

Differentiation of the corium structure begins at the end of the third fetal month, when collagen and elastic fibers are forming within the mesenchymal syncytium. During the last months of fetal life the two permanent layers can first be differentiated: the reticular stratum, rich in collagenous fascicles and bordering the subcutaneous tissue, and the subepithelial stratum or papillary layer, which contains few fibrillar and many cellular structures, bordering on the epidermal stratum germinativum.

In the newborn infant, dermal structure can be viewed as being still in transition from the loosely built, fiber-poor extracellular gel of the fetus to the collagen-rich adult dermis of leather-like consistency (7). The pars papillaris is not yet uniformly shaped, lacking typical surface relief of the adult papillary layer. Only in the palmar and plantar regions are papillary bodies fully developed at birth. On all other skin areas, maturation is delayed beyond early infancy. At 3 months of age, the surface layer of the dermis is still formed by a loosely built cellular network of little specific structure, hardly suggestive of developing papillary shape.

The most obvious changes in the development of the corium are those due to the filling up of the reticular stratum with collagen, a process continuing as long as growth goes on. There is a parallel rise in fiber water and an increase of skin thickness.

# Chapter II

# DEVELOPMENT OF SWEAT GLANDS AND SEBACEOUS GLANDS COMPOSITION OF SWEAT AND SEBUM

## DEVELOPMENT OF SWEAT GLANDS

### Eccrine Sweat Glands

Eccrine or merocrine glands (e-glands) are present over most of the body surface. Their secretory portion (closed coils) is located in the dermis, and the tubular portion (duct) winds its way up through the epidermis to a separate opening at the surface of the skin (Fig. 4). There is no connection of these glandular structures to hair follicles (as in apes).

Eccrine sweat glands are fully developed after the 28th week of gestation, but only a small fraction are endowed with secretory activity at the time of birth. No new glands are formed postnatally, although the proportion of functional to nonfunctional structures is said to increase during the first two years of life and to remain relatively constant thereafter. Furthermore, glands able to secrete sweat in response to stimulation and those unable to do so are not distinguishable morphologically.

Since the total number of glands remains unchanged, their density per unit of surface area is bound to decrease with the expansion of the body surface during growth. In extensively growing regions, such as trunk and extremities, eccrine glands are spread further apart than on the relatively slow-growing face. If measured at the same site, e.g., the thigh, the changes in density with advancing age are as follows (140):

| Age | Glands/cm$^2$ | |
|---|---|---|
| Fetus, 24 weeks | 2970 | ±610 |
| Fetus, 7 months | 1730 | 70 |
| Neonates, full-term | 1560 | 50 |
| Infants, 11-18 months | 500 | 80 |
| Adults, average | 120 | 10 |
| Adults, 73-77 years | 105 | 20 |

The ratio of eccrine sweat glands to pilosebaceous glands (hair follicles) is characteristic for each body region and shows little variation with age during extrauterine life; for the face, for instance, the ratio is 1:3, on trunk and extremities, 3.5:1.

Phylogenetically, the eccrine sweat glands on palms and soles are the oldest ones. Their function was originally a mechanical one; elicited by emotional stimuli (grasping reflex of Darrow [36]) , the secretions served to moisten the animal's paws and to make them stick more easily to grabbed objects. Even in man, the e-glands on palms and soles respond primarily to psychic stimulation (mental sweating) ; those on forehead and axilla to both psychic and thermal stimuli; and those of the rest of the body surface produce only thermal sweat (77a) .

The structural characteristics of eccrine glands, with their "large pale" and "small dark" types of cells, have recently been demonstrated in electron microscopic studies by Ellis (46) .

## Apocrine Sweat Glands

In contrast to the ubiquitous eccrine glands, apocrine sweat glands (a-glands) are restricted to special skin areas. The main site is the axillary region, where the numerous, large glands form a dense aggregate known as the axillary organ of Schiefferdecker (119) . It may attain a thickness of 3.5 mm and is palpable as a kind of cushion, especially in females, who have a greater number of glands than males. The skin area equipped with these amassed glands is approximately that which we will subsequently refer to as axillary vault (Fig. 12) . In contrast, the axillary fossa has no aprocrine glands. Some eccrine sweat glands are present in the entire axillary region.

Other sites of apocrine glands are the anogenital region (labia majora, groin, mons pubis, linea alba, perianal area) ; the external auditory canal (ceruminal glands) ; the ciliary bodies (Moll's glands) ; and the areola of the mammary skin. In all these areas, a-glands are limited in numbers, size, and development, and are rarely activated. The pubic glands have been called "anatomic relics," physiologically inert (75) .

Apocrine sweat glands develop from and remain associated with hair follicles (Fig. 4) ; together with the sebaceous glands, these structures form the apo-pilo-sebaceous unit. Each apocrine glandular duct opens into the upper portion of a hair shaft, through which the apocrine sweat passes to the surface of the skin. The initial budding of the a-gland from the hair follicle occurs around the 14th to 15th fetal week, but the most extensive development takes place between the sixth and eighth fetal month, with differentiation of the characteristic features of secretory coil and excretory duct (77b) .

But even at birth the development is still incomplete and remains so throughout infancy and childhood. Structural maturation occurs sometime before or during adolescence, leading to functional activation with the onset of sexual maturation.* Only in the ear canal are the a-glands fully developed

---

* Adolescence starts with that stage in which penis and testes begin their spurt of growth in the boy and the breast in girls. It ends when full maturity is reached. Puberty is defined as a point when the adolescent boy or girl is capable of procreating.

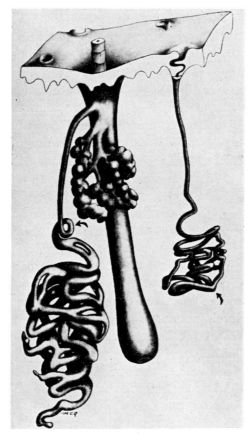

FIGURE 4. Stereogram of an eccrine sweat gland on the right, and an apocrine sweat gland on the left of a hair follicle. From Montagna (95). (Reproduced with permission of the author and Academic Press.)

and functional at birth, possibly because they are under a different endocrine control than apocrine glands on other sites (71).

As compared to eccrine glands, mature a-glands are larger, and the coiled tube of the secretory portion is much wider, appearing somewhat acinous in shape, so that the duct seems to begin only outside the coil. The retained anatomic continuity with the hair follicle has been stressed before. The secretory cells of the coil form a single layer in the apocrine gland, but two layers in the eccrine gland. The most significant single histologic peculiarity of a-glands, however, concerns the process of sweat discharge from the secretory cells into the lumen. In order to deliver the sweat they have produced, the cylindric cells of the a-gland thrust forth their distal portion into the tubular lumen, the projected cytoplasm is decapitated and delivered along with the secretions into the tubules (hence the name "apocrine"). Soon the cell structure is restored and sweat production can be resumed.

## Evolutional Aspects

Available evidence, old and new, indicates that apocrine sweat glands can be distinguished from e-glands on the basis of functional anatomy, their differential responsiveness to exogenous adrenergic and cholinergic stimulation, and the properties of their secretions. At the same time, one should be aware that some features of eccrine structure and function have been found in a-glands. Such findings should not be considered as militating against the belief that there are two distinct categories of human sweat glands. This distinction is fully justified and should be maintained, in spite of objections voiced by Kuno (77c). As the most eminent advocate of this view, Rothman (116a) conceived of apocrine glands as being equipped with a dual mechanism of secretion, namely, the predominating apocrine type, and the merocrine type which operates intermittently and feebly. In addition, there is a congruent dualism of a-gland innervation, adrenergic for the apocrine type of secretion, and cholinergic for the rudimentary merocrine mechanism. The capacity of such dual responses is a unique feature of apocrine sweat glands. This concept is the more attractive as it conforms to long-held views regarding the evolutional development of sweat glands. In all mammals except man the chief sweat glands are of the apocrine type, secreting particulate substances rather than fluid alone (77d). From this primitive form has evolved the eccrine type of gland which produces only watery fluid and is found all over the surface of the human body. In contrast, the apocrine sweat glands, restricted to a few areas of the human skin, represent the less evolved forms, which quite plausibly show features of the more primitive secretory mechanism.

In 1922, Schiefferdecker (119) suggested that a human race showing wider distribution of a-glands over the body surface would be at a lower stage of evolution than ethnic groups whose a-glands are confined to a few areas. According to this criterion, he found the following ranks in the order of advancing evolution: Australians, Chinese, Cameroons, Germans. In 1960, Hurley and Shelley (71) concluded that the greater quantities of apocrine sweat produced by Negroes as compared to whites (in response to adrenergic, mental, and mechanical stimulation) "reflect the racial superiority of the Negro."

Observations of comparative anatomists lend credence to the belief that apocrine glands are related phylogenetically to the scent glands of some animals. Of considerable interest are suggestions that the mammary gland is a descendent of apocrine glands. Pertinent clinical evidence includes the occurrence of accessory mammary glands at the site of the axillary apocrine organ; and the development, late in pregnancy, of nodular axillary structures connecting through a palpable, cord-like tract with the ipsilateral mammary gland (153). Both apocrine and mammary glands undergo involution simultaneously after the menopause; and cystic changes, if they appear in the mammary glands, develop also in the apocrine glands (29, 129).

Further details on apocrine gland function may be found in the monograph of Hurley and Shelley (71).

## COMPOSITION OF SWEAT

Sweat constituents can be identified qualitatively either histochemically within the secretory cells or ducts, or by spot tests performed on the sweat-bearing skin surface, or analytically on small amounts of collected sweat.

Quantitative measurements of sweat components can be made on sweat produced by local or systemic, thermal or pharmacologic stimulation and collected quantitatively by means of gauze pads, filter paper, or glass capillaries. Obviously, sweat taken up from the skin surface may be contaminated with constituents of the surface film.

Some exceptional analyses have been performed on sweat collected through catheterization of individual sweat glands (71) or single orifices on the corny layer (165).

In addition to the difficulties of procuring pure sweat, there is the problem of procuring "normal" sweat. We have learned, for instance, that the kind of sudorific stimulus (64) as well as the rate of sweat flow (48, 81) affects the composition of the delivered sweat.

The influence of age and development on sweat composition remained largely unexplored until Darling and diSant' Agnese, in 1953, discovered an abnormally high chloride and sodium content in sweat of children afflicted with cystic fibrosis of the pancreas (35). Since that time, the literature reflects a growing interest in the developmental factors affecting composition of eccrine and apocrine sweat.

### Eccrine Sweat

The reaction of eccrine sweat varies between pH 4 and 6. As a clear, aqueous, hypotonic solution with an average freezing point of —0.32C, eccrine sweat of the average adult contains 99% to 99.5% water, and 0.5 to 1% solids, half inorganic salts, half organic compounds. Urea accounts for half the organic substances, and NaCl for most of the inorganic ash. At high secretion rates (and in cystic fibrosis) solute concentration may increase to such a degree that the sweat becomes almost isotonic with blood.

Data on age-dependent alterations in electrolyte composition are listed in Table 5, which shows comparable measurements in sweat collected from the skin after sweating was induced by pilocarpine iontophoresis according to the method of Gibson and Cooke (51). It appears that chloride levels remain very similar throughout postnatal life once the higher values prevailing dur-

TABLE 5
AVERAGE ELECTROLYTE CONCENTRATIONS IN ECCRINE SWEAT OF
INFANTS, CHILDREN AND ADULTS*

| | Cl mEq/L | Na mEq/L | K mEq/L |
|---|---|---|---|
| Newborn infants[1] | | | |
| 1st day | 39 | 36 | 8 |
| 2nd day | 34 | 35 | 9 |
| 3rd day | 30 | 28 | 10 |
| 4th day | 24.5 | 30 | 11 |
| Infants, over 5months[1] | 21 | 19 | 13 |
| Infants, 1-12 months[2] | | | |
| males | | 10.7 | 10.7 |
| females | | 11.4 | 12.8 |
| Children, 1-5 years[2] | | | |
| males | | 17.9 | 10.2 |
| females | | 16.7 | 11.2 |
| Children, 6-10 years[2] | | | |
| males | | 16.5 | 11.1 |
| females | | 20.6 | 9.8 |
| Subjects 5 mos.-19 years[3] | | | |
| (median age 11 years) | 21 | | |
| Adults 20-85 years[3] | | | |
| (median age 35 years) | 27 | | |
| Adults 20-60 years[2] | | | |
| males | | 51.9 | 7.5 |
| females | | 36.5 | 10.0 |

All determinations made on sweat obtained by pilocarpine iontophoresis.
[1]according to Stur (136);      [2]according to Lobeck and Huebner (80);
[3]according to Lieberman and Kellogg (179).

ing the newborn period have receded. Sodium concentration is high in the newborn infant, decreases markedly in early infancy, remains low throughout childhood, and rises slowly throughout adolescence and early adulthood to or above the neonatal level. In contrast, potassium levels do not differ appreciably with age.

In sweat produced by intradermal injection of methacholine, the sodium concentration has been found to be lower in prepubertal children than in adults (1). A steady rise of sweat sodium throughout and beyond adolescence is corroborated by the reported increase of the Na/K ratio in thermal sweat from 1.24 in children under 9 years of age to 3.25 in adults over 30 years old (58).

As far as other mineral constituents are concerned, it can only be stated that the small amounts of calcium, magnesium, phosphorus, and sulfates as found in adults are also present in the sweat of children.

The few reported measurements of organic compounds in children (30, 52) fall within the wide range of concentrations found in adults, namely, 12 to 16mg/100 ml sweat for urea, 45 to 350 mg for lactic acid, and 65 to 850 mg for amino acids (as leucine equivalents) (116c). Analyses made by Stur (136) on sweat of 100 neonates showed an average urea concentration of 21%

as compared to 54% in children over 5 months of age, indicating a definite trend of sweat urea to increase during early childhood.

Eccrine sweat contains glycogen, but neither lipids, protein, nor iron are present.

## Apocrine Sweat

Activated shortly prior to adolescence, a-glands elaborate adult-type secretions apparently from the very beginning. The chemical composition of apocrine sweat—a subject of intense interest to dermatologists for half a century—is not yet precisely known, nor are the quantities of identified constituents. The obstacles which hamper analysis of pure apocrine sweat are even greater than in the case of eccrine sweat, since the former must be collected from the axilla where both types are being discharged onto the skin surface.

Actually, only data on apocrine sweat obtained by cannulation of single follicles or examined histochemically within the glandular tissue can be considered as reliable. The main characteristics of apocrine sweat can be defined as follows:

1. A-gland secretions are discharged as an odoriferous, turbid or milky fluid which dries like glue to form a light-colored plastic solid.

2. Apocrine sweat is a hypotonic solution, with a freezing point variously found between —0.1 and —0.48C, as compared to —0.56C for plasma (84).

3. Apocrine sweat has a more alkaline pH (5.5 to 7.0) than eccrine sweat (4.0 to 6.0). The only contention that both types of sweat have a similar pH when delivered to the skin is based on the finding of an apocrine pH range between 5 and 6.5 as determined by indicator strips (129).

4. Only a-glands and their secretions contain iron, estimated at 6 to 10 mg/ml sweat.

5. Apocrine sweat collected from the axilla shows fluorescence in ultraviolet light, as does apocrine gland tissue when examined by ultraviolet light microscopy. Some of the fluorescent material (lipid particles) in surface sweat may be part of the sebaceous gland secretion (116a). Eccrine sweat never shows fluorescence (129), while the cytoplasm of eccrine glands contains sudanophilic droplets which are fluorescent (116b).

6. Proteins are regularly demonstrable in apocrine sweat, but not in eccrine sweat.

For reasons given above, no definite information is available on measured quantities of apocrine sweat constituents. It is known, for instance, that urea may be excreted by a-glands, especially when blood urea is high, but we do not know the average normal urea level. Estimates of lipid material are likewise lacking. Ammonia nitrogen content is exceedingly higher than in body sweat (148).

Less alkaline phosphatase activity is said to be demonstrable in a-glands than in e-glands (22), while acid phosphatase does not occur in either type of sweat glands. Acetylcholine esterase is consistently found around the secretory cells of eccrine glands, while its presence in a-glands remains questionable. Axillary apocrine glands are devoid of glycogen, while a-glands of other regions may contain small amounts of glycogen (96).

## SEBACEOUS GLANDS AND SEBUM

As appendices of hair follicles, these acinous glands are distributed over the entire skin surface, except soles, plantar surfaces of toes, side surfaces of feet and palms, palmar surfaces of fingers and palmar halfs of the interspaces of fingers. The sebaceous glands are located in the deeper layers of the corium and the upper portion of the subcutaneous tissue.

Each gland represents a multilobulated structure which connects through a short duct with the distal portion of the follicular hair canal, from which it has grown out. There are also free or isolated glands, not connected with a hair follicle; they occur mainly where skin adjoins mucous membranes, for instance on palpebrae (Meibomian glands).

The mechanism of sebum secretion is of the holocrine type; the secretory cells disintegrate during the formation of sebum, and the resulting amorphous mass of fat and cell debris moves into and through the follicular canal to the surface where it spreads over the horny layer. Glandular size and amount of secretion vary with the skin area; face, scalp, neck, and upper chest are well known to clinicians as the sites of lavish production of sebum.

In the newborn infant, sebaceous glands are well developed and histologically not distinguishable from those of adults. The glands are functional even before birth (94b), but the production of sebum remains extremely small during infancy and early childhood. Later, secretory activity rises with increasing production of androgens (113).

If judged by the fat content of hair, secretion during the age period of 11 to 13 years is three times higher than in children of 4 to 7 and 7 to 10 years, but of the same order as during the 15- to 25-year period. Activity is highest during the age from 26 to 35 years, but regresses greatly with old age (116f).

Age has also a significant effect upon the cholesterol content of hair fat. Eckstein (45) found 9% to 12% total cholesterol in children aged 2 to 13 years, and only 1 to 5% in adult hair. Nicolaides and Rothman (100) not only confirmed these differences but found that the concentration of squalene (an unsaturated hydrocarbon alcohol) in hair fat is three to four times higher in adults than in children; the molar ratio of cholesterol/squalene was 9.6 in 6- to 12-year-old boys, as compared to 0.856 in male adults.

Sebum levels have also been roughly estimated by nephelometric assays of ether-soluble substances collected from the skin surface. Thus Emanuel (47) found the amount of "sebum fat" to vary characteristically not only with skin

site but also with age. His average measurements expressed as mg fat/2 cm²
are as follows:

|  | On Forehead | On Chest | On Epigastrium |
|---|---|---|---|
| In neonates, 1–2 days | 0.33 | 0.06 | 0.07 |
| In children, 2–12 years | 0.09 | 0.02 | 0.007 |
| On young men | 0.25 | 0.15 | 0.095 |

The high values present in neonates recede soon, conforming to the decrease
of the glands' size.

After onset of adolescence, sebum production in Negroes is about twice
that in whites, in both sexes. The influence of sex is still a matter of con-
troversy.

*Chapter III*

# PROPERTIES OF THE SURFACE FILM

The exterior of the horny layer of the epidermis is enveloped in a thin film of liquid which intimately apposes flexural creases, ridges, furrows, and follicular orifices. The cover projects into the interstices of the cornified layers (137). The matter composing the film is largely derived from products of epidermal tissue metabolism and from sweat and sebum residues.

## COMPOSITION

The surface film consists of aqueous and lipid material. The lipids contain emulsifying agents, mainly cholesterol and wax alcohols, which produce an "oil in water" system when the aqueous phase is in excess, and a "water in oil" system when the fatty phase is in excess (137). Under certain conditions, the fatty and water-soluble components may also be present in a mosaic-like arrangement (132).

Formation of the surface emulsion proceeds continuously; it is not conditioned by the presence of visible sweating.

The aqueous phase is supplied by what we know as insensible sweating: invisible droplets of sweat emerging from the follicular orifices, and moisture penetrating through the horny layer to the surface. In this way, sweat constituents and water-soluble substances of the epidermis become constituents of the aqueous phase of the surface emulsion.

The lipid material consists of fatty substances of sebaceous secretions or is derived from the continual decomposition of the keratin layers; in the axillary region, aprocine sweat contributes some lipid matter. Exogenous contamination may be an additional source of fatty material.

We have listed in Table 6 some of the important constituents, together with the probable source of origin. However, such a differentiation is at best relative. In general, surface lipids have been considered to resemble tissue lipids in composition. As in recent chromatographic studies on the structure of unsaturated fatty acids, samples of surface lipids rather than tissue samples have been analyzed to elucidate skin lipid structure. Obviously, such a correlation does not always prevail. For instance, phospholipids are an essential part of the skin's textural fats, but they are not found in the surface film because they disintegrate with the advancing metamorphosis of viable epidermal cells into dead cornified elements. Another example concerns the presence of only minimal, if any, amounts of sebum on the skin of neonates.

TABLE 6
CONSTITUENTS OF THE SURFACE FILM AND THEIR PROBABLE
DERIVATION

| Constituents | PRESENT (+) OR ABSENT (−) IN | | |
| --- | --- | --- | --- |
| | Sweat (eccr.) | Stratum Disjunctum | Sebaceous Secretions |
| Lactic acid | + | − | − |
| Amino acids | + | + | − |
| Dicarboxylic acids | + | + | − |
| Basic amino acids | + | + | − |
| Ammonia | + | + | − |
| Free fatty acids (water-sol.) | − | (−) | + |
| Free choline | (+) | + | ? |
| Na | + | + | (+) |
| K | + | + | + |
| Ca | − | + | (+) |
| Mg | + | + | ? |
| Cl | + | + | ? |
| P | + | + | + |
| Reducing sugars | + | + | − |
| Lipids | − | + | + |
| Cholesterol | − | + | + |
| Water-insol. fatty acids | − | (+) | + |

Parentheses indicate that data are doubtful.

Information on age-dependent alterations in the composition of the surface film is notoriously lacking. We do not know, for instance, whether the high cholesterol content of hair in children (three times higher than adults) is reflected in similar differences in surface lipids between children and adults.

Until recently, only H$^+$ activity had been measured directly on the skin surface. With the advent of cation- and anion-sensitive electrodes, the way has been opened to determine Na$^+$, K$^+$, Ca$^{++}$, and Cl$^-$ activities on the surface coat. Thus far, such measurements have been made with the sodium (53,125) and chloride electrode (154), but only on skin areas where profuse sweating had been induced, i.e., in sweat deposits. Activity measurements on the dry skin are mentioned in one study (53).

## Factors Responsible for the Acid Skin pH

While the acid reaction of the surface had already been noted by Heuss (68) in 1892 and by Unna (150) in 1910, the first authentic investigations on skin pH were published by Schade and Marchionini (84,118) in 1928/29. Applying one of the early electrometric methods, they demonstrated the existence of a physiologic "Säuremantel" (acid mantle) of the skin. Almost at the same time, Herrmann and Fürst (63) reported similar findings in a colorimetric study of skin pH.

By determining the surface pH we actually measure the H-ion concentration (activity) in the aqueous phase of the surface emulsion. Present views (86,116d,130–132, 143) regarding the source of the acidic solutes can be summarized as follows: the acid pH values obtaining to most of the body surface are the result of the composite effects of dissociated, water-soluble constituents present in epidermal tissue and eccrine sweat. Lactic acid ranks first among them, followed by the dicarboxylic amino acids (glutamic and aspartic acid). Of the higher fatty acids, only the low-molecular propionic, butyric, pentanoic, and hexanoic acids are water soluble and could influence the pH; whether they actually do so is still in doubt. Sebaceous secretions other than fatty acids do not contribute to the acidity of the film surface (refer to Table 6).

## Buffering Systems

Acidity of the "open" surfaces varies physiologically within the pH range of about 4 to 6, in the majority of subjects between 4.5 and 5.8. Only in this restricted sense may one speak of a homeostatically controlled surface pH. Neutralization of acidifying and alkalinizing effects from within and without is attained by several systems: First, the lactic acid-lactate system, provided by sweat; it has a highly efficient buffering capacity at pH 4 to 5. Second, there are the amphoteric amino acids secreted by sweat glands, with an undefined maximum of buffering power. Third, free amino acids of the stratum disjunctum play an important role; they account for almost 40% of the water-soluble substances extracted from this stratum by analysis of graded skin strippings. Fourth, the proteins of the horny layer have to be considered. Since they have an isoelectric point of pH 4.1 and are insoluble in water, their part, if any, in contributing to buffering capacity must be limited.

Although the existence of buffering systems seems to be assured, the mechanism of their combined function and their total capacity is still uncertain. There is the additional question as to what extent carbon dioxide contributes to the maintenance of the surface pH under physiologic conditions. Little is known about the operating of a $CO_2/HCO_3$ system. Burckhardt's studies (23,24,26) have provided ample evidence that alkali when brought onto the skin surface, is neutralized in part by carbon dioxide diffusing continuously from the epidermal layers underneath. But it has not yet been shown whether the steady diffusion also plays a role in the normal acidification process.

## SURFACE pH AND EPIDERMAL TISSUE pH

Szakall (143) was able to perform pH measurements with the electrode on the surface of the various epidermal layers exposed by consecutive strippings with transparent tape. He found the following reactions at different depths of the epidermis:

| Skin surface | pH 4–6 |
|---|---|
| Stratum corneum disjunctum | 6.4 |
| Stratum lucidum | 4.5 |
| Stratum granulosum | |
| Stratum germinativum | |
| Stratum basale | 7.2 |
| Dermis | 7.2 |

It is most remarkable that the acidity of the stratum lucidum can increase to such a high level. One will also notice the high pH of the stratum disjunctum, exceeding the values for the subjacent layer and for the adjoining surface film.

Burckhhardt *et al.* (27) could demonstrate a similar pattern by applying nitrazine to the skin surface as a tracer. When penetrating into and through the epidermis, the indicator solution exhibits directly observable color changes corresponding to the changes in tissue pH.

It is poorly understood how these differential pH levels come about. In all likelihood, one of the essential factors is the influence of the part of the epidermis known as barrier zone (p. 10). One of the best known functions of this barrier is the maintenance of differential degrees of hydration in the various epidermal layers. As compared to the adjoining zones above and below, hydration is optimal in the barrier itself; its water-holding capacity rests on the integrity of the lipid-protein complexes. Removal of lipid and water, leaving the protein, completely destroys the barrier functions. The defensive action against overhydration and dehydration extends even to the surface film, since preservation of "the relative minute water quantity present at any time in the stratum corneum is of supreme importance for the physiologic function of the surface" (65). In the light of these findings it is conceivable that the mechanism by which the barrier controls hydration is also implicated in the control of epidermal tissue pH and surface pH.

For further details of the fine structure and physiologic significance of the barrier membrane, the reader is referred to the presentation by Rothman and Lorincz (117). Marculli (87) conceives of the stratum corneum as a complex of many barriers with varying capacity, each penetrant encountering different barriers depending on its chemical and physical properties.

We do not know of any data on physiologic peculiarities of the barrier zone in infants and children.

## PROTECTIVE FUNCTIONS

Not so long ago, the relation between skin acidity and antibacterial defense was a highly controversial subject. Some considered certain organic acids as exerting specific antibacterial action, while others held that the overall pH of the surface was responsible for the self-disinfection of the human skin (19,

32,105,107). Today there is sufficient evidence to support the broader concept that surface defense against invasion of microorganisms is accomplished by the combined efforts of desiccation, epidermal desquamation, water-soluble acidic constituents, the acid pH, and fixed antibodies (86).

Obviously, electrolytes play an important role in pH-dependent regulatory processes, including hydration of the surface film and subjacent cellular structures. The lipid phase of the film affords protection against removal and penetration of water soluble compounds. After preliminary defatting of the surface, the release of such substances by immersion in water (of hand and forearm) proceeds at a rate sixty times faster than it normally would (133). However, the lipid film cannot prevent some swelling of horny layers after prolonged contact of the skin with water (74).

As a consequence of new evidence and changing concepts, Marchionini's original designation of the surface film as "acid mantle" is now replaced by such terms as "lipid mantle," "buffering coat," "electrolyte mantle," or "complex varnish," whenever such connotations are preferable.

## Vernix Caseosa

As long as the body is bathed in amniotic fluid during intrauterine life, skin surface and fluid can hardly be separated by a kind of film resembling the coat which is interposed between epidermis and surrounding air during extrauterine life. Indications are that by the seventh month of gestation, at the latest, epithelial disintegration is in progress, with fatty degeneration of keratinized cells and shedding of dead cornified matter. The amniotic fluid may contribute to maceration which these products undergo on the broken, desquamating surface.

When emerging from the liquid medium at birth, the body surface is more or less concealed by the combined residues of fluid and structural debris, which condense into what is known as vernix caseosa: a layer of macerated, grayish-yellow, greasy, viscous material. Beneath this spread and entrapped in it are the deranged thin layers of epidermis.

Like amniotic fluid, vernix has a weakly alkaline pH close to 7.4 (if measured within one hour after birth). The dry matter of vernix contains 47% to 75% ether-soluble substances. The lipids are probably "in the main not of glandular origin" but products of fatty decomposition of epidermal cells (116e). Two thirds of the lipids are saponifiable; 21% of the latter fraction consist of hydrocarbons, notably squalene (31). Glycogen and eleidin have also been found to be present, but no keratohyalin.

# Chapter IV

# MEASUREMENT OF SKIN pH

## COLORIMETRIC PROCEDURES

"Chemical pH indicators function by exhibiting a color intensity or transmission property characteristic of the acid-base ratio of the solution to which they are added" (90). Such indicators are usually described as behaving like weak acids or bases. For example, an indicator acid, HIn, would dissociate into H⁺ and In⁻ according to the dissociation constant, with either HIn or In⁻ being colored. Within certain limitations, fully discussed in monographs on the subject (90,149), the color intensity is determined as

$$\log \ (C_{In}/C_{HIn})$$

where C is concentration. The colored sample is compared against a known standard solution of the indicator whose pH has been defined electrometrically.

Colorimetric pH determinations with indicators can give highly accurate results when carried out *in vitro* in transparent aqueous solutions; some difficulties will arise with colloidal solutions or suspensions, or when measurements are to be made on surfaces of living organs.

Colorimetric pH tests on the skin originally required the use of three different indicators, each covering a different pH range (127). A relatively large skin area was needed for applying the prescribed amounts of the three indicators, each of which had to be taken up and transferred to a separate test tube to be diluted to standard volume with water. Comparison was with corresponding standard solutions of the indicators in similar test tubes.

Another procedure was that of foil colorimetry, in which indicator-impregnated sheets of absorbing material were tested with a drop of water which had been placed on the skin and taken up after 5 minutes (82).

### Test with Combined Indicator Solution

For our own colorimetric studies we adopted the method of Bernstein and Herrmann (14), who used an indicator solution* covering the pH range from 2.5 to 9.5. Directions are as follows: Skin cleaning of any kind is prohibited for 6 hours prior to the test. One drop of indicator solution is pipetted onto the test site, stirred briefly with a glass rod, and taken up into

---

* Universal Wide Range Indicator (Harleco). Contains 0.1 gm. of powdered Parstains Indicator in 75 ml. of methanol (41 per cent) in water, with sufficient n-NaOH added to effect solution. Harleco, 60th Str. & Woodland Ave., Philadelphia, Pa.

a l-inch piece of capillary tubing (0.5 mm in diameter) .* The liquid in the tube is then matched with the corresponding color on a wide-range color chart supplied with the indicator; the pH value of the matching color is noted by two observers. Readings are taken in bright daylight, or in artificial blue-bulb illumination. Transparent samples can be read most accurately; samples taken up from the axillary region may show turbidity due to admixed apocrine sweat, prohibiting satisfactory comparison with the color chart. In this case, the test has to be repeated when sweating has subsided.

## POTENTIOMETRIC METHODS

The earlier electrometric pH measurements on the skin were carried out by means of hydrogen (84) , quinhydrone (78,84,121,141) , or antimony (13) electrodes. The errors inherent in the use of these types of electrodes have been eliminated to a great extent by the construction of "glass electrodes" with selective hydrogen-ion sensitivity. These pH glass electrodes were the first of a number of cation-sensitive electrodes to be made from glasses containing oxides of silica ($SiO_2$) , lithium ($Li_2O$) , and aluminum ($Al_2O_3$) as major components. Systems of glass plus reference electrodes have been successfully employed for the determination of hydrogen, sodium, potassium, and $pCo_2$ in biologic fluids (90,125) .

Soon after its introduction in 1930, the pH glass electrode was applied to acidity measurements on the skin (15,78,158) and has gradually replaced the earlier methods of potentiometric skin pH determination. Recent models are of high sensitivity; they are available in various sizes and shapes, single and in combination with reference electrodes. Some of these models, including microelectrodes, are particularly designed for pH measurements of blood *in vitro* and on internal surfaces *in vivo* (125) ; others may be selected for pH tests on the skin.

### Test Performance

Our measurements were made with the General Purpose Glass Electrode (Beckman No. 41260) and a calomel reference electrode (Beckman No. 39170) , connected by 30-inch leads to a portable potentiometer (Beckman N-2) . The two electrodes, fitted onto a metal holder, were slipped over a vertical rod attached to one side of the apparatus.

While in the rod-attached holder, the electrodes can be lowered to dip into solutions, or they can be taken off the rod for use on the skin surface.

The electrode system is standardized at room temperature at the beginning of each test session with buffer solutions of pH 4 and 7, with the temperature adjustment set at the temperature of the buffer solution. Rechecking of proper standardization is carried out repeatedly during serial tests.

---

* Coagulation Capillary Tubes, No. 5- 962, Fisher Scientific Comp. Springfield, New Jersey.

No cleansing of the test area is permitted during a 6-hour period preceding the test. The skin site is moistened with 1 drop of saturated aqueous KCl solution to sustain a conducting film between tips of the electrodes, which are then placed on the moistened site, vertically to the surface. The holder permits sufficient leeway to approximate the electrode tips to within one-fourth inch of each other. Stabilized readings can usually be obtained within 10 to 15 seconds. No adjustment is made for temperature differences between buffer standard and skin surface, a practice which has been generally followed in such studies (see p. 35).

Equally precise readings have been obtained when the "bridging" through KCl is omitted and the electrodes are dipped into distilled water each time before they are applied to the skin (5). Apparently, this procedure effects sufficient hydration of the surface film to secure a natural salt bridge.

Tests for average pH levels of the acid mantle are to be made on "exposed" or "open" skin sites, preferably those of chest, back, and limbs (exterior or flexor surfaces). Since the pH varies from area to area, even between contralateral sites, the significance of calculated mean pH values will increase with the number of sites tested.

As a rule, skin areas where surfaces are in appositon (e.g., intertriginal and interdigital spaces), should not be included as sites for measuring average skin acidity. Readings on these sites should be evaluated separately (see p. 35).

## INTERPRETATIONS

### The Meaning of pH

$[H^+]$ = hydrogen ion concentration

pH = negative logarithm to the base 10 of $[H^+]$ in equivalents per liter

Example: In a N/500 solution of HCl, $[H^+]$ is 0.002 or
$2 \times 10^{-3}$ equivalents per liter;
pH = $-\log (2 \times 10^{-3})$; since log 2 equals 0.3,
pH = $+3 - 0.3 = 2.7$.

While buffering systems are responsible for acid-base balance, pH is an index of the position of balance. The use of the term pH obscures the magnitude of change in $[H^+]$. For instance, though a change of pH by one unit signifies a tenfold increase or decrease in $[H^+]$, alterations in $[H^+]$ are not equivalent when pH is shifted by an equal number of units above or below 7.4, the neutral point: $[H^+]$ increases more by a shift of pH to 5.4 than it decreases by a shift to 9.4.

The need for thinking in logarithmic terms when interpreting pH measurements is obvious. It is realized that the pH notation makes it difficult to correlate $[H^+]$ with concentrations of other substances commonly expressed

in terms of mEq/L, or even to make comparisons between solutions of different [$H^+$]. Many feel that the veil of pH contributes to the mystery surrounding the subject of acid-base balance in medicine. Yet, one cannot unveil pH,
as Mattock says (89).

Here the question comes up whether it is permissible to take the arith-
metic mean of logarithmic functions (or the geometric mean of $H^+$ concentrations). The fact that biostatisticians don't hesitate to use "mean skin pH
levels," does not answer the question in the affirmative, since no justification
is offered, with one exception (104). Unfortunately, the statement by Moore
that "utmost precaution should be observed in the reporting of pH (geometric) averages" is not amplified by showing a way out of the dilemma. Discus-
sions dealing with this problem may be found in Nature, 155:463, 1945 (J. H.
Gaddum) ; in Trans. Inst. Mining Met., vol 61 and 62, 1952–1953 (H. E.
Sichel) ; and in Gastroenterology, 45:458, 1963 (E. W. Moore). These refer-
ences are quoted from G. Eisenman (ed.) , Glass Electrodes for Hydrogen and
other Cations, New York, Marcel Dekker, 1967.

### The Meaning of Skin pH Measurements

Variations in skin pH may extend over the same range under normal and
pathologic conditions. This precludes attempts to define the value of an individual reading as normal or abnormal in the customary way. Instead,
evaluation of skin pH measurements is concerned with recognizing certain
trends in variations, i.e., the frequency distribution of higher and lower
readings within an almost unchanging range. Thus pH averages, rather than
individual readings, become indices of the acid-base balance on a given skin
area. If determined on multiple sites of healthy individuals, these averages
yield the physiologic pH pattern of the surface, which, in turn, may permit
to define and speak of abnormal patterns. Except for one special situation
(see p. 79) , a single pH measurement has no diagnostic significance.

This is why skin pH studies are bound to deal with serial measurements
procured in such a way as to be amenable to statistic analysis. The task is one
of determining means of acidity (see p. 47) and to define the variables which
influence these means. Such determining factors are skin site, environment,
body temperature, age, developmental age, sex, race, sexual maturation, apart
from the effects of pathology. Ideally, two groups of subjects have to be tested
which are strictly comparable but for one variant. This kind of design will
not always be feasible, but the fewer the inherent variants, the more accurate
will be the evaluation.

Serial measurements are usually reported in terms of ranges and means.
Computation of both subject means (from readings on all sites tested in the
subject or subjects) and site means (from readings on the same site in all
subjects) is called for.

## *Effect of Extraneous Factors*

Attention must be given to the influence of liquids, ointments or lotions which may have been applied to the test area for cosmetic or therapeutic reasons on the days preceeding the test. Even washing with soap or detergents within 12 hours prior to the pH determination, may result in false readings.

On surfaces which are in apposition (in the various skin folds, groin, axilla) or tightly covered most of the time (soles), acidity tends to be lower than on open skin areas. According to long held views (14,62,63,84,105,118,), the pH rises at these sites as a consequence of impaired evaporation and stagnation of sweat: concentration of acids on the surface is prohibited, ammonia formation is facilitated, and epidermal keratolysis enhanced. In addition, lack of cleanliness may decrease acidity in these areas. However, some doubts have been raised whether impaired evaporation is the main factor antagonizing surface acidification, since a rise in pH also takes place in skin tissue upon evaporation at 35C and might be related to formation of condensation products of sugar-amino acids.

The increment in skin pH on the above sites is as evident in children as in adults, as documented in Table 10 for full size neonates (groin, antecubital fossa, axilla); in Table 14 and 15 for 2-to 12-month-old infants (groin, axilla); in Table 17 for 3-to 6-year-old children (axilla); in Table 19 for preadolescent boys (axilla); and in Table 29 for children up to 15 years (between toes).

The influence of ambient and skin temperature on skin acidity is generally regarded as insignificant under usual environmental conditions, but supporting evidence is scanty. We have therefore made some comparative pH measurements in 12 low-birth-weight infants aged 2 to 8 days.

All infants were maintained in incubators and could be assumed to be under stabilized thermal conditions. Skin pH and skin temperature were determined, respectively, with the glass electrode and a thermistor probe on one lower leg, through a porthole of the incubator. Then the same leg was exposed up to the middle of the thigh through an opened porthole to the cooler air of the nursery. After 30 to 40 minutes of exposure, pH and temperature readings were repeated on the same site tested previously inside the incubator. The following measurements were recorded:

| *Ambient Temp.* | | *Skin Temp.* | | *Skin pH* | |
|---|---|---|---|---|---|
| incub. | room | before | after | before | after |
| | | | exposure | | exposure |
| C | C | C | C | | |
| 32.0 | 24.4 | 36.3 | 34.7 | 6.0 | 6.0 |
| 30.5 | 26.1 | 33.5 | 32.2 | 6.2 | 6.1 |
| 30.3 | 25.6 | — | — | 5.7 | 5.8 |
| 31.6 | 23.8 | 36.1 | 33.2 | 6.4 | 6.4 |
| 31.7 | 25.6 | 35.6 | 34.2 | 6.9 | 6.6 |
| 32.4 | 25.0 | 35.4 | 32.2 | 6.2 | 6.0 |

| Ambient Temp. | | Skin Temp. | | Skin pH | |
|---|---|---|---|---|---|
| *incub.* | *room* | *before* | *after* | *before* | *after* |
| | | *exposure* | | *exposure* | |
| 32.4 | 25.0 | 35.6 | 33.7 | 6.3 | 6.0 |
| 32.0 | 25.1 | 34.8 | 32.3 | 6.2 | 6.2 |
| 32.0 | 25.1 | 34.6 | 33.0 | 6.2 | 6.3 |
| 33.0 | 24.4 | 35.2 | 32.7 | 6.2 | 6.0 |
| 28.8 | 24.2 | 35.8 | 35.2 | 5.3 | 5.3 |
| 32.2 | 23.2 | 34.7 | 32.3 | 6.0 | 5.9 |

It appears that changes in ambient temperature leading to a drop in skin temperature by even 3.2C are not associated with significant alterations in skin pH.

Finally, one should be aware that surface pH may decrease with a rise in sweating rate, since eccrine sweat acidity is directly related to sweat flow (48, 81).

## COMPARISON OF COLORIMETRIC AND POTENTIOMETRIC READINGS

Insufficient work has been done to establish how accurate are measurements of pH on the skin surface. In the experience of most workers, e.g., Beare *et al* (5), the accuracy of the glass electrode method is not better than $\pm$ 0.2 pH unit. In our own hands, the described electrode method has a reproducibility (95% confidence limit of a single determination) of 4.1%. For a mean skin pH of 5.5, for instance, the 95% confidence limit would be $\pm$0.22 pH unit. This value compares well with the coefficient of variation of many chemical micromethods commonly used for blood analysis (101), but is far below the degree of accuracy, namely $\pm$ 0.01 pH unit, attained with the glass electrode in serum pH determinations.

There can be no doubt that colorimetric readings show wider scatter than potentiometric values as determined at the same site. Indeed, the relationship between the two kinds of readings is less predictable than was originally thought. We performed comparative measurements, on the same site, in 44 subjects, with a total of 77 dual readings. The results show that the difference between paired values varies with their position on the pH scale: Readings differ the least, namely by less than $\pm$ 0.5 pH, in the range between pH 6 and 7. When colorimetric values fall into the range of pH 3 to 5, measurements with the electrode read 0.5 to 1.0 pH units higher; when colorimetric values are exceeding pH 7.0, potentiometric readings are consistently lower by up to 1 pH unit. No curve can be fitted to express these relations mathematically. Likewise, experimentally induced changes in skin pH, when followed up with the indicator, tend to be more drastic than when determined potentiometrically (64). The spectrum of potentiometric readings appears to be compressed in comparison to that of corresponding colorimetric values.

On the other hand, we will present evidence to show that the characteristic trend of pH changes due to physiologic or other factors, is revealed with equal consistence and significance by measurements with the glass electrode and the described indicator method, not withstanding the difference between absolute values. We reiterate: A comparison of colorimetric with potentiometric studies is admissible and useful if restricted to the evaluation of "trends," i.e., of the relative changes in pH with respect to a given variant. However, single (individual or mean) colorimetric and potentiometric values are neither comparable nor interchangeable as criteria of interpretation.

Finally, we should mention an element of uncertainty which is inherent even in potentiometric measurements on living surfaces. Unwanted bioelectric potentials which are difficult to eliminate are liable to cause complications (90). Furthermore, when cation activities are measured on the surface of the cerebral cortex (93), there is uncertainty whether the fluid interspace, through which the electrodes are in contact with the cortical surface, represents a continuation of the extracellular space of the parenchyma or a combination of capillary transudation and fluid from the surface. Similar doubt must arise regarding the potentials recorded from the skin surface: To what extent are they altered by the structural continuity "persistent down to the molecular level" and by the diffusion of the connecting salt-bridge into the tissue? Perhaps such questions are irrelevant to the clinical value of skin pH measurements, but we should be aware that the problem exists.

# Chapter V

# SURFACE pH OF THE HEALTHY SKIN
# FROM BIRTH THROUGH INFANCY

## NEWBORN PERIOD

Taddei (145) reported in 1935 that the markedly acid reaction characteristic of the healthy skin surface in man, was missing in the newborn infant. He measured the pH colorimetrically on the back of 120 infants at ages ranging from 1 to 20 days and found the means for the different days to vary from pH 6.5 to 6.8 with no correlation between age and pH. The mean for prematurely born infants among the series was 6.4. We now know that there is indeed no acid mantle present at birth, but that the development of surface acidification follows a different pattern than that implied in Taddei's results.

### Full-term Infants

#### *Colorimetric Data*

Our first study (9) was carried out on 213 full-term infants aged 1 hour to 30 days. They included 106 males and 107 females; there were 68 Caucasians, 62 Negroes, and 83 Puerto Ricans. Measurements were taken on 3 sites: shoulder, where the deltoid covers the acromion; armpit, in an area roughly corresponding to axillary vault plus fossa; and abdomen, about 1 inch lateral to the navel.

The scattergram of Figure 5 illustrates the distribution of pH readings by age, without differentiating between skin areas. During the first 24 hours after birth, there is a marked preponderance of values above pH 6.0, with 58 readings exceeding pH 7.0. On the second day of life, there is a shift towards higher acidity, with values below pH 6.0 accounting for 50.7% of all readings. On the third and fourth days, the proportion of markedly acid readings has further increased. This proportion remains relatively constant during the following nine days. Finally, during the third and fourth postnatal weeks, an almost uniformly acid pattern prevails, with only an occasional value exceeding pH 6.0.

In order to define the influence of age and site on surface pH, we have classified the 213 subjects into three age groups of comparable size and calculated the mean pH values for each test site in each age group. The results are shown in Table 7; they confirm the trend in pH changes indicated by the scattergram (bottom of Figure 5). The site means in Group II are significant-

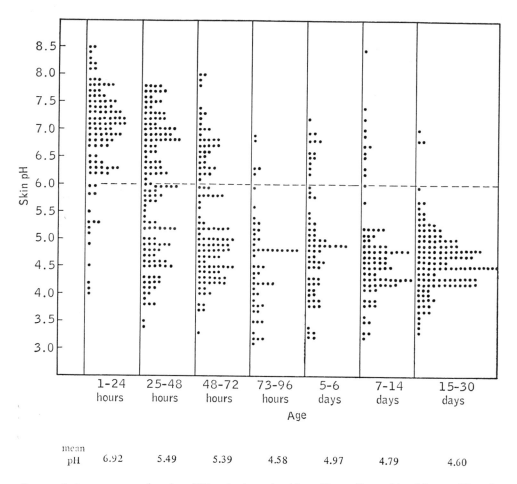

| mean pH | 6.92 | 5.49 | 5.39 | 4.58 | 4.97 | 4.79 | 4.60 |
| --- | --- | --- | --- | --- | --- | --- | --- |

FIGURE 5. Scattergram showing 729 colorimetric skin pH readings (shoulder, axilla, abdomen) in 213 full-size infants by age groups. From Behrendt and Green (9). (Reproduced with permission of *Amer. J. Dis. Child.*)

ly lower than the corresponding means in Group I, but are not different from those in Group III. It will also be noticed that the mean pH on the abdominal wall is higher than on shoulder and axilla, especially in Groups I and II.

There are no sex differences with respect to age-dependent pH changes, as documented in Table 8. Even the site means for males and females are very similar, except for the axilla in Group I.

An attempted resolution of our measurements into differential means for Caucasians, Negroes, and Puerto Ricans suggests that there is no difference between these groups with respect to the decline of skin pH with age. However, the lack of racial homogenuity among the subjects designated as Puerto

Ricans does not permit any valid conclusions, and we have omitted documentation of these data.*

TABLE 7

SKIN pH OF 213 FULL-SIZE INFANTS RELATION TO AGE AND SITE (COLORIMETRIC SERIES)*

| Age Group | No. of Subjects | | | Test Site | No. of Tests | Skin pH | | |
|---|---|---|---|---|---|---|---|---|
| | Total | M | F | | | Range | Mean | ±S. D. |
| I 1-48 hours | 79 | 43 | 36 | shoulder | 78 | 3.4–8.2 | 5.97 | 1.27 |
| | | | | axilla | 77 | 3.5–8.5 | 6.27 | 1.27 |
| | | | | abdomen | 73 | 4.5–8.2 | 6.81 | 0.85 |
| | | | | all 3 sites | 228 | 3.4–8.5 | **6.34** | 1.33 |
| II 3-6 days | 61 | 29 | 32 | shoulder | 61 | 3.2–7.1 | 4.68 | 1.02 |
| | | | | axilla | 60 | 3.0–7.8 | 4.78 | 1.02 |
| | | | | abdomen | 59 | 3.1–7.9 | 5.41 | 1.00 |
| | | | | all 3 sites | 180 | 3.0–7.9 | **4.95** | 1.01 |
| III 7-30 days | 73 | 34 | 39 | shoulder | 73 | 3.3–7.0 | 4.46 | 0.59 |
| | | | | axilla | 73 | 3.2–7.2 | 4.77 | 0.72 |
| | | | | abdomen | 70 | 3.9–7.2 | 4.89 | 0.81 |
| | | | | all 3 sites | 216 | 3.2–7.2 | **4.70** | 0.69 |

*From Behrendt and Green (9).

TABLE 8

SKIN pH IN RELATION TO AGE AND SITE: COMPARATIVE READINGS IN MALE AND FEMALE FULL-SIZE INFANTS*

| | Males | | | Females | | |
|---|---|---|---|---|---|---|
| | No. of Tests | Skin pH | | No. of Tests | Skin pH | |
| | | Mean | ±S.D. | | Mean | ±S.D. |
| AGE GROUP I 1-48 hours | | | | | | |
| shoulder | 42 | 6.04 | 1.15 | 36 | 5.89 | 1.36 |
| axilla | 42 | 6.16 | 1.35 | 35 | 6.41 | 1.14 |
| abdomen | 41 | 6.83 | 0.78 | 32 | 6.77 | 0.93 |
| AGE GROUP II 3-6 days | | | | | | |
| shoulder | 29 | 4.67 | 1.12 | 32 | 4.67 | 0.97 |
| axilla | 28 | 4.60 | 1.14 | 32 | 4.75 | 0.91 |
| abdomen | 28 | 5.35 | 1.00 | 31 | 5.46 | 0.95 |
| AGE GROUP III 7-30 days | | | | | | |
| shoulder | 34 | 4.56 | 0.81 | 39 | 4.37 | 0.46 |
| axilla | 34 | 4.64 | 0.70 | 39 | 4.82 | 0.64 |
| abdomen | 34 | 4.86 | 0.77 | 36 | 4.91 | 0.83 |

*Computed from the same colorimetric measurements as Table 7.

* Since the material of all our studies includes a large proportion of Puerto Ricans, evaluation of race as a variant will be omitted throughout this presentation. Occasionally, a differentiation between whites and nonwhites has been attempted.

## Potentiometric Data

THE FIRST WEEK AFTER BIRTH (BELFAST SERIES). Beare *et al.* (5, 6) measured the skin pH potentiometrically at thirty-four body sites of each of 203 full-term infants of 1 to 8 days of age, 100 males and 103 females. Table 9 gives the subject means by age groups. There is a definite trend of the pH to decrease from the first to the fifth day, followed by a slight rise from the fifth to the eighth day, a trend similar to that found in our colorimetric study.

Table 10 shows the means for each of the 34 sites for all subjects. Here the following points are of interest: Flexor surfaces have consistently higher pH readings than the corresponding extensor surfaces, with differences ranging from 0.33 to 0.8 pH unit. On the average, dorsum of hand and elbow, and upper arm (extensor) have the most acid reactions, while groin, scalp, and forehead are relatively more alkaline. Smaller, though significant differences exist between contralateral areas in 5 of the 15 sites tested bilaterally.

In an analysis of covariance, the authors found age and site to be the most significant sources of variation. At the ages concerned, sex plays no important role. Furthermore, the changes with age described in Table 9 for the subject means are equally discernible in the site means. All 34 test areas had first-day means greater than the means for any other of the subsequent seven days, and in two thirds of the comparisons the differences were statistically significant. The course of mean pH levels during the first week of life, as charted by the authors of the Belfast series, is reproduced in Figure 6.

Thus, the trend demonstrated in our own study for three sites, applies to practically the entire skin surface of the neonate.

THE SECOND TO FOURTH WEEK OF LIFE. We have listed in Table 15 our potentiometric measurements taken at four sites of each of fifteen infants aged from 12 to 28 days. It is interesting to note that the mean pH of 5.5 for these sites is lower than the mean of 6.06 for the 34 sites found for the eighth day

### TABLE 9
MEAN SKIN pH OF FULL-SIZE NEWBORN INFANTS BY AGE. (BELFAST SERIES; POTENTIOMETRIC READINGS ON THIRTY-FOUR SITES)*

| Age (Day of Life) | No. of Infants | No. of Tests | Skin pH | |
| --- | --- | --- | --- | --- |
| | | | Mean | ±S.D. |
| 1st | 12 | 408 | 6.77 | 0.15 |
| 2nd | 24 | 816 | 6.27 | 0.11 |
| 3rd | 24 | 816 | 6.03 | 0.11 |
| 4th | 28 | 952 | 6.12 | 0.10 |
| 5th | 34 | 1156 | 5.86 | 0.09 |
| 6th | 19 | 646 | 5.93 | 0.12 |
| 7th | 38 | 1292 | 6.01 | 0.09 |
| 8th | 24 | 816 | 6.06 | 0.11 |
| 1st-8th | 203 | 6902 | 6.08 | 0.04 |

*From Beare et al. (6).

TABLE 10

POTENTIOMETRIC pH READINGS IN 203 FULL-SIZE NEONATES, BELFAST SERIES: SITES RANKED IN ORDER OF SITE MEANS*

| Rank Order | Site R—Right L—Left | | Site Mean pH | Rank of Homogeneous Site Means[1] |
|---|---|---|---|---|
| 1 | Dorsum hand | L | 5.56 | 1 |
| 2 | Elbow point | R | 5.57 | 2 |
| 3 | Elbow point | L | 5.60 | 3 |
| 4 | Upper arm ext. | R | 5.60 | 4 |
| 5 | Dorsum hand | R | 5.64 | 5  5 |
| 6 | Upper arm ext. | L | 5.75 | 6  6 |
| 7 | Popliteal fossa | R | 5.85 | 7  7 |
| 8 | Wrist flexor | L | 5.89 | 8  8 |
| 9 | Ankle anterior | R | 5.89 | 9  9 |
| 10 | Poplit. fossa | L | 5.96 | 10  10  10 |
| 11 | Abdomen | | 5.99 | 11  11  11 |
| 12 | Retroaur. fold | L | 6.01 | 12  12  12 |
| 13 | Wrist flexor | R | 6.01 | 13  13  13  13 |
| 14 | Sole | R | 6.03 | 14  14  14  14  14 |
| 15 | Perianal area | | 6.03 | 15  15  15  15 |
| 16 | Thigh anterior | R | 6.06 | 16  16  16  16  16 |
| 17 | Palm | L | 6.07 | 17  17  17  17  17 |
| 18 | Axilla | R | 6.12 | 18  18  18  18  18 |
| 19 | Cheek | L | 6.15 | 19  19  19  19  19 |
| 20 | Upper arm flex. | L | 6.17 | 20  20  20  20 |
| 21 | Sole | L | 6.17 | 21  21  21  21 |
| 22 | Ankle anterior | L | 6.17 | 22  22  22  22 |
| 23 | Palm | R | 6.19 | 23  23  23 |
| 24 | Retroaur. fold | R | 6.19 | 24  24  24 |
| 25 | Upper arm flex. | R | 6.19 | 25  25  25 |
| 26 | Axilla | L | 6.24 | 26  26 |
| 27 | Cheek | R | 6.25 | 27  27 |
| 28 | Antecub. fossa | L | 6.28 | 28  28 |
| 29 | Antecub. fossa | R | 6.38 | 29  29 |
| 30 | Thigh anterior | L | 6.39 | 30  30 |
| 31 | Forehead | | 6.42 | 31 |
| 32 | Groin | R | 6.50 | 32  32 |
| 33 | Scalp | | 6.56 | 33 |
| 34 | Groin | L | 6.79 | 34 |

[1]Each column shows ranks of means which are not significantly different by Duncan's test (43). Standard error of a single site mean=0.044.
*From Beare et al. (5).

of life in the Belfast series. This suggests a trend of the pH to further decline, once the initial decrease has taken place during the first week. As to skin sites, the lower abdomen has the least acid mean pH of the four tested areas, while the pH range is very similar on all sites.

The results obtained in this small series compare well with those reported earlier by Arbenz (3) for three areas in 29 infants of the same age group. He found the following potentiometric values:

$$\text{on chest } 4.8\text{--}6.1, \text{ with a mean of } 5.35 \pm 0.33$$
$$\text{on forehead } 4.5\text{--}5.1 \qquad\qquad\qquad 5.30 \quad 0.35$$
$$\text{on axilla } 5.0\text{--}5.7 \qquad\qquad\qquad\quad 5.39 \quad 0.20$$

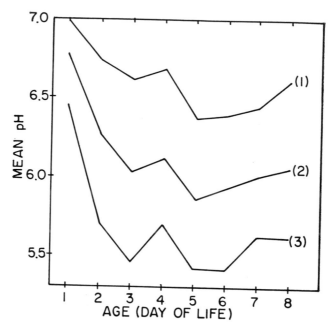

FIGURE 6. Mean skin pH of children of different age. (1), six most alkaline sites; (2), all sites; (3), four most acid sites. Potentiometric measurements. From Beare *et al.* (6). (Reproduced with permission of the authors and *Brit.J.Derm.*)

## Summary

The course of the mean pH level in full-term infants from birth through the fourth week of life is charted in Figure 7, showing the means of colorimetric and potentiometric readings. The curve of colorimetric values has a deeper slope. Starting at almost identical points near neutrality on the first day, the tracings are 0.6 pH unit apart on the third day, and about 0.5 unit apart throughout the third and fourth week. The trend is evidenced by both curves, but is more drastically brought out by the colorimetric values. The potentiometric readings come closest to actually prevailing H-ion concentrations on the surface.

## Infants of Low Birth Weight

As reported recently (55), we have measured skin pH potentiometrically in a series of 127 infants of low birth weight* whose postnatal age at the time of testing ranged from 1 to 28 days. In each infant, the skin pH was determined at four sites: top of shoulder, volar aspect of the right forearm, lateral aspect of the lower left leg, and upper abdomen, midway between navel and ster-

---

* Low birth weight is defined as 2,500 gm or less; prematurely born infants are those with a gestational age of less than 37 completed weeks.

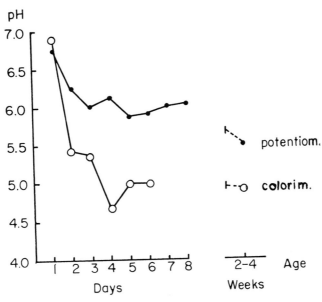

FIGURE 7. Physiologic changes in mean skin pH of full term infants during the first month after birth: comparative *potentiometric* and *colorimetric* measurements.

TABLE 11
COMPOSITION OF LOW-BIRTH-WEIGHT SERIES

| Age, Day of Life | No. of Subjects | Sex | | Race | | Birth Weight[1] Group | | | Gestation Age[1] Group | | | |
|---|---|---|---|---|---|---|---|---|---|---|---|---|
| | | M | F | W | NW | I | II | III | A | B | C | D |
| 1 | 10 | 3 | 7 | 2 | 8 | 3 | 5 | 2 | 2 | 6 | 1 | 1 |
| 2 | 10 | 6 | 4 | 2 | 8 | 2 | 6 | 2 | 6 | 2 | 1 | 2 |
| 3 | 10 | 4 | 6 | 6 | 4 | 4 | 5 | 1 | 7 | 1 | — | 2 |
| 4 | 10 | 3 | 7 | 4 | 6 | 3 | 5 | 2 | 7 | 1 | 2 | — |
| 5 | 10 | 4 | 6 | 6 | 4 | 1 | 5 | 4 | 5 | 5 | — | — |
| 6 | 10 | 6 | 4 | 3 | 7 | — | 10 | — | 7 | 2 | 1 | — |
| 7 | 10 | 7 | 3 | 2 | 8 | 1 | 8 | 1 | 5 | 4 | 1 | — |
| 8 | 10 | 5 | 5 | 1 | 9 | 2 | 5 | 3 | 2 | 4 | 4 | — |
| 12 | 2 | — | 2 | 1 | 1 | — | 2 | — | 1 | — | — | 1 |
| 13 | 5 | 1 | 4 | 2 | 3 | 2 | 2 | 1 | 2 | 2 | — | 1 |
| 14 | 3 | — | 3 | — | 3 | 1 | 1 | 1 | 1 | 1 | — | 1 |
| 15 | 6 | 3 | 3 | 3 | 3 | 1 | 1 | 4 | 3 | 2 | 1 | — |
| 16 | 3 | 2 | 1 | — | 3 | 1 | 1 | 1 | 3 | — | — | — |
| 17 | 2 | 1 | 1 | 2 | — | 1 | 1 | — | 1 | 1 | — | — |
| 18 | 3 | 1 | 2 | 1 | 2 | 1 | 2 | — | 2 | — | 1 | — |
| 19 | 4 | 3 | 1 | 1 | 3 | — | 4 | — | 1 | 2 | 1 | — |
| 20 | 1 | 1 | — | 1 | — | — | 1 | — | 1 | — | — | — |
| 21 | 8 | 4 | 4 | 4 | 4 | 2 | 6 | — | 2 | 4 | 2 | — |
| 22 | 1 | 1 | — | — | 1 | — | — | 1 | — | — | 1 | — |
| 24 | 1 | 1 | — | 1 | — | — | 1 | — | 1 | — | — | — |
| 25 | 2 | 1 | 1 | 1 | 1 | — | 1 | 1 | 2 | — | — | — |
| 26 | 2 | 1 | 1 | 1 | 1 | — | 1 | 1 | — | 2 | — | — |
| 27 | 2 | 2 | — | 2 | — | 2 | — | — | — | 1 | 1 | — |
| 28 | 2 | 1 | 1 | 1 | 1 | 1 | 1 | — | — | 1 | 1 | — |
| Totals | 127 | 61 | 66 | 47 | 80 | 28 | 74 | 25 | 61 | 41 | 18 | 7 |

[1]For definition, see text: W, white; NW, nonwhite.

num. The majority were born prematurely, the others were of low birth weight but had a gestational age of more than 36 weeks. The composition of the series according to postnatal age, gestational age, sex, and race is given in Table 11. The following classification was used:

> Birth Weight Groups: I, < 1,500 gm; II, 1,500–2,000 gm; III, 2,001–2,500 gm
> Gestational Age Groups: A, < 34 completed weeks; B, 34–36 weeks; C, 37–39 weeks; D, 40 weeks and more.

Subjects listed as white include also white Spanish Puerto Ricans; those listed as non-white comprise North and Latin American Negroes, including Puerto Rican Negroes.

All infants were in incubators since birth and were not removed for testing. Ambient temperature at the time of testing ranged from 30 to 33C for infants in Isolettes, and from 24 to 29C for those in Gordon-Armstrong Units.

## The First Week After Birth

The core of the obtained information concerns the 80 infants tested between the first and eighth day of life. As can be seen from Table 12 and Figure 8, both means and ranges decline markedly from the first to second day, and from the second to third day; to a lesser degree, this decline continues through the subsequent four days. At the eighth day, pH values range between 5.4 and 6.6, with a mean of 5.99, as compared to 6.77 on the first day. The same pH shift toward higher acidity is discernible in the individual site means listed in Table 12. Acidity is lower on the abdominal wall than on the forearm on all but the first 2 days.

## The Second to Fourth Week of Life

Measurements on 12-to 28-day-old infants of low birth weight were ob-

### TABLE 12
### SKIN pH OF EIGHTY NEONATES OF LOW BIRTH WEIGHT: SITE MEANS AND SUBJECT MEANS*

| Age, Day of Life | Shoulder | | Forearm | | Abdomen | | Lower Leg | | All 4 Sites | |
|---|---|---|---|---|---|---|---|---|---|---|
| | Mean pH | SE | Mean pH | SE | Mean pH | SE | Mean pH | SE | Mean pH | SE |
| 1 | 6.72 | ±0.10 | 6.62 | ±0.10 | 6.85 | ±0.10 | 6.50 | ±0.07 | 6.67 | ±0.05 |
| 2 | 6.27 | 0.11 | 6.29 | 0.08 | 6.36 | 0.10 | 6.30 | 0.09 | 6.31 | 0.05 |
| 3 | 6.23 | 0.06 | 6.18 | 0.12 | 6.31 | 0.08 | 6.31 | 0.05 | 6.26 | 0.04 |
| 4 | 6.18 | 0.07 | 6.18 | 0.08 | 6.29 | 0.05 | 6.21 | 0.09 | 6.21 | 0.04 |
| 5 | 6.02 | 0.08 | 5.96 | 0.06 | 6.06 | 0.07 | 6.04 | 0.07 | 6.02 | 0.04 |
| 6 | 6.05 | 0.09 | 5.98 | 0.07 | 6.13 | 0.07 | 6.01 | 0.07 | 6.04 | 0.04 |
| 7 | 6.15 | 0.06 | 5.94 | 0.04 | 6.21 | 0.08 | 5.98 | 0.07 | 6.07 | 0.04 |
| 8 | 5.99 | 0.08 | 5.85 | 0.06 | 6.02 | 0.11 | 5.89 | 0.06 | 5.04 | 0.03 |

10 subjects in each age group; potentiometric measurements.
*Modified from Green et al. (55).

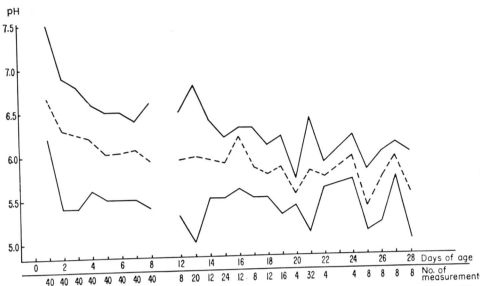

FIGURE 8. Means and ranges of skin pH (four sites) plotted against age: 127 infants of low birth weight. Potentiometric readings. From Green *et al.* (55). (Reproduced with permission of *Amer. J. Dis. Child.*)

tained from 47 subjects. When examining the curves for this series in Figure 8, one will detect a trend of the pH mean and range to further decline (below the values prevailing at the end of the first week). There is a difference of pH 0.4 between the means for day 8 and day 28.

*Analysis of Covariance*

The 508 readings collected from the 127 infants of low birth weight, comprising 1-to 28-day-old subjects, were submitted to statistical analysis as follows:

pH readings were classified according to the factors of sex, race, and site, with 2, 2, and 4 levels, respectively. Concomitant variables were age, age squared (because of possible nonlinearity), birth weight, environmental temperature, gestational age, gestational age squared, and gestational age × age. An analysis of covariance was performed with the above factors and variables according to the method of Harvey (60), using the program of Hurst (72).

Tests of significance were made on the above factors and regression weights, applying the 5 percent level of significance. Wherever tests indicated "significance", multiple comparisons between levels were made in order to pinpoint actual differences, removing the effect of covariables. Furthermore, tests for the equality of regression coefficients (parallelism) for different levels of sex were performed according to the method used by Carol in a previous study (15). Thus, an interaction between sex and a covariate was determined.

The analysis according to this design was made on a computer (IBM 1620). Multiple comparisons for age at different gestational levels were specifically programmed and evaluated by the computer.

The results are given in Table 13. They prove, first, that the influence of age squared is highly significant, and second, that the decline of pH during the first 4 postnatal week is not a linear function of advancing age. No other factor influences the regression during the first 28 days as much as age. Gestational age as such, plays no significant role as a factor determining the postnatal trend of pH changes. However, the influence of gestational age × age is very highly significant.

Neither birth weight nor ambient temperature has a significant influence. However, sex, race, and site, after adjustment for the covariates, play a significant role. The skin pH is higher in Negroes than in whites, and higher in females than in males; the confidence interval for the average sex difference being 0.099 to 0.025. Sex does not interact with age in shaping the decline of skin pH.

All tested skin areas participate in the acidification process, but the apparent intersite differences are significant only between abdomen (with the highest mean pH) and forearm (with the lowest mean pH), the true mean difference lying within the interval 0.048 and 0.24.

The trend of measured pH changes during the first 28 days can be mathematically defined by theoretical curves based on the predicting variables of age and gestational age. Such a computation has been performed for the gestation ages of 24, 28, 32, 36, and 40 weeks. The obtained curves are reproduced in Figure 9, together with the equation from which the required data were secured. The tracings are parabolic, commencing at and diverging from the same point at day 1. This conforms to the finding that gestational age as

TABLE 13
## SKIN pH MEASUREMENTS OF 127 NEONATES OF LOW BIRTH WEIGHT: ANALYSIS OF COVARIANCE*

| Source | df | Means Square | Variance Ratio | P |
|---|---|---|---|---|
| Sex | 1 | 0.3313 | 4.340 | <0.050 |
| Site | 3 | 0.4077 | 5.340 | <0.005 |
| Race | 1 | 0.3026 | 3.960 | <0.050 |
| Sex-site | 3 | 0.0123 | <1.000 | >0.050 |
| Sex-race | 1 | 0.0028 | <1.000 | >0.050 |
| Site-race | 3 | 0.0500 | <1.000 | >0.050 |
| Sex-site-race | 3 | 0.0132 | <1.000 | >0.050 |
| Age | 1 | 0.0267 | 0.350 | >0.050 |
| Age squared | 1 | 3.5854 | 46.920 | <0.001 |
| Temperature | 1 | 0.0089 | 0.116 | >0.050 |
| Gestational age | 1 | 0.1775 | 2.520 | >0.050 |
| Gestational age squared | 1 | 0.1156 | 1.510 | >0.050 |
| Gestational age × age | 1 | 1.9727 | 25.810 | <0.001 |
| Residual | 489 | 0.0764 | — | — |

-Birth weight does not appear in this tabulation. Limitations as to the total number of covariates which can be tested according to the applied program made it necessary to eliminate one variable. Birth weight was dropped since it had been tested in an exploratory analysis of variance and found to be not significant (P>0.1).
*From Green et al. (55)

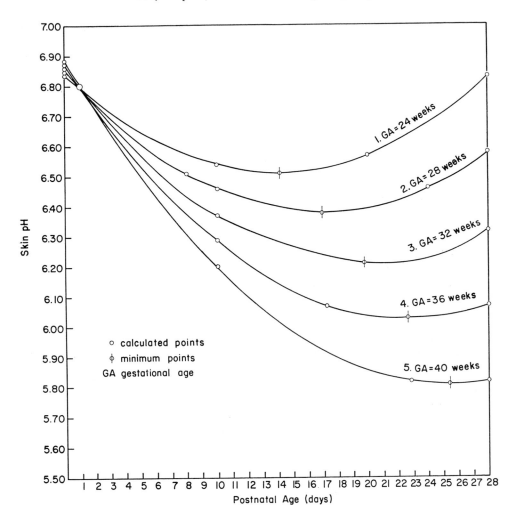

FIGURE 9. Mathematical model showing estimated changes in skin pH during first 28 days after birth for infants of low birth weight of different gestational ages. Potentiometric measurements.

Equations: $pH = \beta_2 t^2 + (\beta_1 + \beta_3 C) + a$ (parabola)

where $\beta_1 = 0.0094333$
$\beta_2 = 0.001646$ $\Bigg\}$ are weights indicating relative importance of age, age squared,
$\beta_3 = 0.0023299$ and gestational age $\times$ age, respectively.

C is gestational age
t is postnatal age
a is a constant.

Curve 1: $pH = (0.001646) t^2 - (0.0464843) t + 6.8448$
Curve 2: $pH = (0.001646) t^2 - (0.0558039) t + 6.8541579$
Curve 3: $pH = (0.001646) t^2 - (0.0651235) t + 6.8635$
Curve 4: $pH = (0.001646) t^2 - (0.0744431) t + 6.872797$
Curve 5: $pH = (0.001646) t^2 - (0.0837627) t + 6.8821167$

such is not of significant influence; if it were, the curves would run more or less parallel commencing at separate points.

Various tests were done on the pH values to see if the day-to-day changes in pH were significant during the first week of life. For the tested gestational ages of 28, 32, 36, and 40 weeks, the drop in pH from day to day was found to be indeed significant.

In summary, the statistical analysis with regard to the covariates of age and gestational age indicates that the former as well as the latter factor in conjunction with age are of highly significant influence.

### Horizontal Study

Nine infants of low birth weight were examined initially at one of the first 3 days after birth and retested at varying intervals during the first month of life. As illustrated in Figure 10, mean pH values show a downward trend with advancing age in all but one instance. The figures for the different ages are similar to those of the vertical study.

### Low-Birth-Weight vs. Full-Size Neonates

The trend of the pH to decline during the postnatal period is as obvious in our colorimetrically tested mature infants as in the prematurely born infants tested with the glass electrode. However, for a numerical comparison, our results on low-birth-weight infants have to be correlated with the Belfast series, which provide the only available data on full-term neonates tested with the glass electrode. Still, the sites tested in the Belfast series include only one (abdomen) of the four sites examined in our premature infants, and the Belfast series are representative of the homogenous white population of that country. Inspite of these differences, we have listed side by side in Table 14 the mean pH values from both studies, for each day of the first week, together with additional values for older infants taken from our potentiometric data. The similarity of the trend of pH to decline with age is as impressive as are the almost identical changes from day to day.

## Mechanism of Postnatal pH Conversion

An interpretation of the observed decline in surface pH during the immediate postnatal period should bring into focus the similarity of this decline in full-term and prematurely born neonates. At birth, and as long as the skin is covered with remnants of the vernix, the surfacee pH reflects the neutral or alkaline reaction of this lipid coat. We have shown (9) that readings taken after cleansing of the test site with water or alcohol are as high as before removal of the remains of vernix, possibly because the surface of the epidermis proper is in an abnormal state of maceration for some time after birth, being entrapped in what may be called a fixed layer of vernix. With disintegration

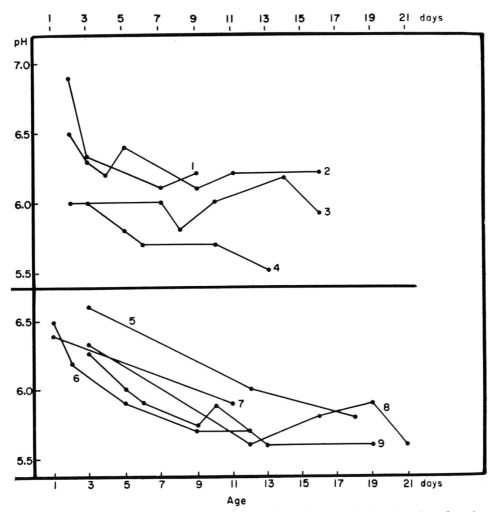

FIGURE 10. Changes in mean skin pH with age (four sites) : individual tracings for nine infants of low birth weight. Potentiometric measurements. From Green *et al.* (55). (Reproduced with permission of *Amer. J. Dis. Child.*)

of this macerated material, epidermal structure and surface continuity are gradually normalized, and the skin can assume normal functional properties, usually around the fifth day after birth. At this time, the surface pH will turn increasingly acid, provided the acidifying mechanism has been operative all along. Available evidence supports such an assumption and speaks against the belief that the pH shift be occasioned by a gradual maturation of an acidifying mechanism which is deficient at birth. The degree of any neonatal dysfunction is supposed to be directly related to the infant's maturity at the time of birth. Instead, we have seen that gestational age is not a significant factor and that acidification proceeds at equal rates and almost identical levels

TABLE 14

CHANGES IN SKIN pH WITH AGE: SUBJECT MEANS FOR FULL-SIZE AND LOW-BIRTH-WEIGHT NEONATES. MEASUREMENTS WITH THE GLASS ELECTRODE

| Age, Day of Life | 203 Full-Size Infants (BELFAST SERIES)[1] | | 80 LOW-BIRTH-WEIGHT INFANTS[2] | |
|---|---|---|---|---|
| | Mean pH | SE | Mean pH | SE |
| 1 | 6.77 ± | 0.15 | 6.67 ± | 0.05 |
| 2 | 6.27 | 0.11 | 6.31 | 0.05 |
| 3 | 6.03 | 0.11 | 6.26 | 0.04 |
| 4 | 6.12 | 0.10 | 6.21 | 0.04 |
| 5 | 5.86 | 0.09 | 6.02 | 0.04 |
| 6 | 5.93 | 0.12 | 6.04 | 0.04 |
| 7 | 6.01 | 0.09 | 6.07 | 0.04 |
| 8 | 6.06 | 0.11 | 5.94 | 0.03 |

[1]From Beare et al. (6).    [2]From Green et al. (55).

in prematurely born and term neonates, for at least 8 days. A maturity-dependent pattern of acidification appears incompatible with our finding that, in many instances, neonates born after 28 weeks of gestation or earlier (with a birth weight of 1,800 gm or less) have the same skin pH as those born at term (with a birth weight of 3,000 gm or more).

Therefore, it seems reasonable to assume that in both classes of neonates, acidification is well under way immediately after birth, but that the acidic substances are barred from reaching the surface by the covering aggregate of extraneous matter. When this cover disintegrates, the various endogenous constituents responsible for acidification can emerge from beneath the surface and formation of the acid mantle can proceed.

Another question is whether sweat gland secretion contributes to acidification at this early age. In the prematurely born infant who is incapable of sweating, this source may be disregarded for the first postnatal week. Full-term neonates have the capacity for thermal sweating, though their threshold is higher than in older infants (21,37,91,92), and insensible sweating could well be a source of acidification. The close similarity of pH patterns found in premature and term babies speaks against this possibility. We have reason to believe that this is not the only indication that the dominant influence of eccrine sweat on surface properties of the skin may be less assured than is commonly believed. (See also Chapter IX.)

## SECOND TO TWELFTH MONTH

In order to trace the development of skin acidity through the remaining 11 months of infancy, we have determined the skin pH potentiometrically on nine sites of 31 healthy full-term infants who were over 1 month of age but not older than 12 months at the time of testing. The results, as listed in the second part of Table 15, suggest that there is no trend of the skin pH to decline further or change otherwise during this age period. The mean pH for the nine sites is the same as for the four sites tested in the preceding age group (documented in the same table). The range of subject means for the 2- to 12-month-old infants extends to equally high levels as in the 12-to 30-day-old subjects, but reaches more acid values than in the younger group.

The degree of variation between site means does not appear to be different in the two age groups. Acidity on the abdominal wall is lower than on all other sites, except for the groin. Furthermore, a comparison with the Belfast data for the first week after birth (Table 9) implies a similar rank of test areas in the order of acidity, with the posterior surface of the knee and the elbow joint showing the lowest pH, and the groin the highest.

That no essential variation in skin pH levels takes place during months 2 to 12 is also apparent from the potentiometric measurements reported by Arbenz (3) for 29 infants between 1 and 10 months of age. He found no differences in the means on corresponding sites between infants of different age within this series, and computed the following site means:

|  | *range* | *mean* | *SD* |
|---|---|---|---|
| chest | 4.8–6.1 | 5.35 | ±0.33 |
| forehead | 4.5–5.1 | 5.30 | 0.35 |
| axilla | 5.0–5.7 | 5.39 | 0.20 |

We have deleted from this tabulation the measurements on the groin because this skin area had been apparently in contact with urine-soaked diapers up to the time of testing. The listed means are very similar to those for the 12-to 30-day-old infants given in Table 14.

TABLE 15
SKIN pH FOR TWO PERIODS OF INFANCY
POTENTIOMETRIC SERIES

| Test Site | No. of Tests | Skin pH | | | |
|---|---|---|---|---|---|
| | | Range | Mean | ±S.D. | |
| Shoulder | 15 | 4.7-6.1 | 5.38 | 0.38 | AGE GROUP: |
| Forearm, volar | 15 | 4.9-5.8 | 5.38 | 0.26 | 12-30 Days |
| Abdomen, lower | 15 | 5.1-6.1 | 5.69 | 0.29 | 15 Full-Size Infants; |
| Lower leg, extensor | 15 | 5.0-6.4 | 5.61 | 0.39 | Range of Subject Means; |
| All four sites | 60 | 4.7-6.4 | 5.51 | 0.36 | pH 5.51-6.00 |
| | | | | | |
| Abdomen, lower | 31 | 5.2-6.8 | 5.82 | 0.35 | |
| Mons pubis | 31 | 5.2-7.1 | 5.78 | 0.36 | |
| Groin, right | 31 | 4.8-6.7 | 5.83 | 0.50 | AGE GROUP: |
| Thigh, anterior, right | 31 | 4.8-6.3 | 5.64 | 0.33 | 2nd-12th Month |
| Thigh, posterior, right | 31 | 4.7-6.2 | 5.51 | 0.37 | 31 Full-Size Infants; |
| Buttocks, right | 30 | 4.8-6.3 | 5.72 | 0.39 | Range of Subject Means: |
| Lower back | 31 | 4.6-6.1 | 5.48 | 0.42 | pH 4.94-6.07 |
| Poplitea, right | 23 | 4.7-6.3 | 5.30 | 0.04 | |
| Elbow point, left | 23 | 4.8-5.8 | 5.27 | 0.28 | |
| All nine sites | 262 | 4.6-7.1 | 5.59 | 0.38 | |

## SUMMARY

The developmental patterns for the first year of life can be described as follows:

1. Immediately after delivery, the neonate's skin surface is of neutral or alkaline reaction.

2. Acidification begins within 24 hours after birth and intensifies with each day of the first week of life.

3. The pH shift from near neutrality to moderate acidity involves the entire body surface.

4. A slight downward trend of the pH level continues throughout the first month of life, while skin acidity remains almost constant throughout the following 11 months.

5. Sequence and extent of acidification are almost identical in full-size and low-birth-weight infants.

6. Throughout, some skin areas are characterized by a higher mean pH than others, regardless of age.

7. While sex is not a source of pH variation in full-term infants, female infants of low birth weight have a higher mean skin pH than low-birth-weight males.

# Chapter VI

# SURFACE pH OF THE HEALTHY SKIN: SECOND THROUGH SIXTH YEAR OF CHILDHOOD

Attempts to chart the trend of changes in skin pH for this period of childhood are hampered by the paucity of pertinent data. Most reported mean values are for subjects whose ages range from early through late childhood. In some instances, children for whom mean values are listed include infants and preadolescents. Although such data may be meaningful for some expressely stated purpose, they are of little value in defining changes associated with the successive stages of growth. Thus, we are left with only the results of measurements which are few in numbers but relate at least, to children of distinct age groups.

## THE SECOND YEAR OF LIFE

We have tested 19 children whose ages ranged from 13 to 24 months at the time of testing. Their skin pH was determined potentiometrically at the same nine sites tested in the series of 2- to 12-month-old infants. The results are listed in Table 16. If they are compared with the measurements of the 2- to 12-month-old infants of Table 15, the close similarity of the pH patterns is clearly discernible. The means for all sites and all subjects are identical in both series. We may conclude that surface acidity is maintained unchanged throughout the transition from infancy to childhood.

Also inserted in Table 16 are the results of colorimetric readings on three sites of 14 children whose ages ranged from 13 to 24 months. We note the marked differences between colorimetric and electrometric site means and realize that the results obtained by the different methods are not directly comparable. Since colorimetric data for the immediately preceding age period of 2 to 12 months are not available, the colorimetric readings for the 13- to 24-month-old children have to be related to those for the 7- to 30-day-old infants of Table 7 and Figure 5. Although not all of the test sites are identical, a comparison shows that the mean pH values remain unchanged from infancy through the end of the second year.

## PRESCHOOL CHILDREN

Skin acidity levels prevailing from the third through the sixth year of life are listed in Table 17, which shows the results of colorimetric determinations on three sites of 84 children. In both sexes, the mean pH is highest on the axillary vault, and very similar on the more acid surfaces of axillary fossa and shoulder. There is no apparent difference between the subject means of males and females. The mean pH value of 4.49 referring to sites of all subjects, almost equals the corresponding colorimetric mean for the second year of life (listed in Table 16). On this basis it may be said that skin acidity undergoes no significant changes during the preschool years.

The only electrometric measurements for this period we can quote are the following data assembled from our records: In 14 children aged 3 to 6 years the mean pH values were:

TABLE 16
SKIN pH FOR THE AGE PERIOD OF THIRTEEN TO TWENTY-FOUR MONTHS

| Test Site | No. of Tests | Skin pH | | |
| --- | --- | --- | --- | --- |
| | | Range | Means | ±S.D. |
| | | Potentiometric[1] | | |
| Lower Abdomen | 19 | 5.0-6.5 | 5.73 | 0.37 |
| Mons pubis | 19 | 4.9-6.8 | 5.57 | 0.57 |
| Groin, right | 19 | 4.9-6.8 | 5.69 | 0.47 |
| Thigh, anterior, right | 19 | 4.8-6.7 | 5.70 | 0.47 |
| Thigh, posterior, right | 19 | 4.9-6.1 | 5.69 | 0.36 |
| Buttocks, right | 18 | 5.2-6.3 | 5.74 | 0.33 |
| Lower back | 19 | 4.7-6.4 | 5.36 | 0.42 |
| Poplitea, right | 17 | 4.6-5.8 | 5.32 | 0.31 |
| Elbow point, left | 17 | 4.9-5.9 | 5.36 | 0.32 |
| All 9 sites | 166 | 4.6-6.8 | **5.57** | 0.41 |
| | | Colorimetric[2] | | |
| Shoulder | 14 | 3.5-4.8 | 4.16 | 0.44 |
| Axillary fossa | 14 | 3.8-5.2 | 4.39 | 0.42 |
| Axillary vault | 14 | 3.4-5.6 | 4.72 | 0.60 |
| All 3 sites | 42 | 3.4-5.6 | **4.43** | 0.49 |

[1]Range of 19 subject means: pH5.18-6.16.
[2]Range of 14 subject means: pH 3.67-4.93.

5.29 ±0.97  on the shoulder
5.52    0.60  on the axillary fossa,
5.53    0.43  on the axillary vault,
5.32    0.52  on all three sites.

Subject means ranged from pH 4.5 to 6.0. These values may be viewed against the potentiometrically determined means which we obtained in children tested during their second year of life, though at different sites (Table 16). Average skin acidity is the same in these two age groups, confirming the results of the above colorimetric measurements.

TABLE 17
SKIN pH FOR CHILDREN OF TWO TO SIX YEARS OF AGE
COLORIMETRIC SERIES

| Site | 84 SUBJECTS | | | 27 MALES | | | 57 FEMALES | | |
|---|---|---|---|---|---|---|---|---|---|
| | Range of pH | Mean .H | S.D. | Range of pH | Mean pH | S.D. | Range of pH | Mean pH | S.D. |
| Shoulder | 3.4-6.5 | 4.33 | ±0.70 | 3.5-5.8 | 4.27 | ±0.63 | 3.4-6.5 | 4.36 | ±0.73 |
| Axillary fossa | 3.4-6.8 | 4.42 | 0.65 | 4.3-5.8 | 4.37 | 0.61 | 3.4-6.8 | 4.45 | 0.67 |
| Axillary vault | 3.4-7.8 | 4.72 | 1.00 | 3.4-6.0 | 4.71 | 0.59 | 3.5-7.8 | 4.73 | 1.15 |
| All 3 sites | 3.4-7.8 | **4.49** | 0.75 | 3.4-6.0 | **4.44** | 0.61 | 3.4-7.8 | **4.52** | 0.81 |

Range of subject means: males, 3.8-5.8; females, 3.6-6.6.

# Chapter VII

# SURFACE pH OF THE HEALTHY SKIN: PREADOLESCENCE AND ADOLESCENCE

Once the child enters school age, patterns of surface pH become dependent on developmental factors rather than age alone. From this time on, alterations in the acidity of the open surfaces lose importance as compared to the gradual formation of "alkaline" isles within the acid mantle. The areas involved are the sites of apocrine glands, primarily the axilla. Marchionini (84) already related the high axillary pH which he found in adults to the presence of apocrine sweat.

The nonacid reaction in the axilla must be distinguished from the diminished acidity often present at sites where surfaces are in apposition, such as intertriginous and interdigital spaces. In these locations, the pH will tend to rise as the result of impaired evaporation of sweat, regardless of the subject's age (p. 35). In the axilla, however, sweat stagnation loses importance as an alkalinizing factor once "alkaline" apocrine sweat is delivered to the surface.

In the initial investigation of healthy children (62) we were still concerned with the influence of chronologic age on skin pH. In tests of subjects of four consecutive age groups (extending from less than 1 year to 15 years), we found a striking similarity of the pH on corresponding sites at all ages, with one notable exception: the axillary readings in subjects older than 7 years showed an increment of pH over the values prevailing among the younger age categories (Figure 11). These measurements revealed for the first time the age period during which a progressive rise of the axillary pH becomes manifest. It was thought that in all likelihood this rise was not age-dependent but due to onset of adolescent development. Arbenz (3) corroborated our data and felt that the increment in pH was coincidental with the development of secondary sex characters.

Thus, the next task was to demonstrate the parallelism between sexual development and pH conversion on the axillary zones. Our studies to be described in the present chapter are proof of this direct relationship and supplement the histologic evidence of these correlations provided by Greulich (56) in 1942. He examined more than 100 samples of axillary skin obtained at autopsy and found that axillary a-glands begin to enlarge shortly before adolescence but do not attain the morphologic maturity of fully operative glands "until puberty is well advanced."*

---

* See footnote on p. 16.

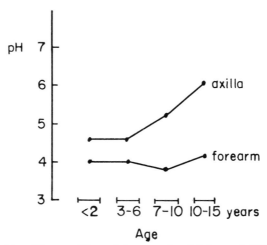

FIGURE 11. Average skin pH on *axilla* and *forearm* in children of different age groups; 30 subjects in the oldest group, 19 subjects in each of the other groups. Colorimetric measurements. Modified from Herrmann *et al.* (62).

## AXILLARY SKIN pH IN RELATION TO MATURITY STATUS

### Assessment of Sexual Development

Maturity rating was based on essentially the same criteria as used by Greulich (57) and Schoenfeld (122). Boys were classified in five maturity groups and girls in four groups, representing the successive stages in the transition from physical immaturity to late adolescence. The external characteristics which served as criteria for classification are as follows:

*Males*

*Group I*: penis, testes, scrotum of infantile size; no evidence of secondary sex characters.

*Group II*: convincing evidence of active growth of penis, testes, scrotum; presence of pubic hair.

*Group III*: further increase in size of sex organs and in amount of pubic hair; appearance of facial and axillary hair.

*Group IV*: amount of pubic hair almost that of adults; size of sex organs increased (corpora cavernosa); facial and axillary hair increased.

*Group V*: sex organs of adult size; sexual hair as in adult; mature body proportions.

*Females*

*Group I*: infantile body proportions; no evidence of secondary sex characteristics; infantile sex organs.

*Group II*: growth of pelvis, budding of breasts and nipples; sparse pubic hair.

*Group III*: pelvis of mature proportions, markedly developed breasts; increased amount of pubic hair; moderate amount of axillary hair.

*Group IV*: almost fully developed breasts; axillary and pubic hair almost as in adults; almost mature body proportions; menarche.

## Test Sites

In practice, only the axillary region is a feasible site for exploring pH changes due to deposition of apocrine sweat. Our pH measurements in the axillary space have been made on two different sites (Figure 12). These are best exposed when the subject lies on the examination table, places his right palm under his head, and rotates his body to the left until the right axilla faces upward. In this position, the depression of the armpit is shallow, and the axilla presents itself as an almost, plane surface.

a) AXILLARY VAULT: This site is well within the area overlying the apocrine organ, carrying axillary hair. For the test, electrodes or indicator fluid are applied within an area in the center of the axillary fold, which continues upward into the pectoral deltoid groove. If the person is in the upright position and the arm is raised at an angle of 45 degrees (Figure 13), this test site corresponds to the apex of the vault. Accurate location of the site is essential; axillary hair does not interfere with testing.

b) AXILLARY FOSSA: This site was selected on the assumption that it represents an eccrine area outside the a-gland-carrying vault. The anterior border is the lateral edge of the lower portion of the pectoralis major; the posterior border is the edge of the latissimus dorsi. The changing depth and width of

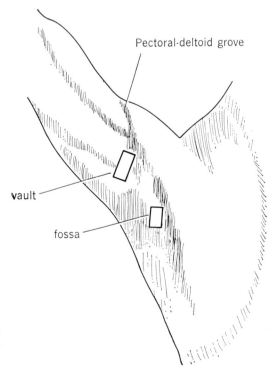

FIGURE 12. Axillary *vault and fossa*: sites for testing surface pH. From Behrendt and Green (8). (Reproduced with permission of *Amer. J. Dis. Child.*)

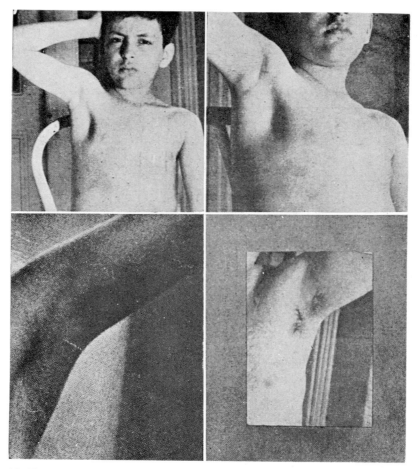

FIGURE 13. Photographs of the axillary space of four boys of different maturity, illustrating the surface anatomy of vault and fossa. From Behrendt and Green (8). (Reproduced with permission of *Amer. J. Dis. Child.*)

the fossa, particularly in girls, are noteworthy; its site is indicated in Figures 12 and 13.

c) SHOULDER: This is an exclusively eccrine area; it is tested where the deltoid covers the acromion.

## Axillary pH Patterns in Males

These colorimetric test series (8,10) included 502 boys whose ages ranged from one month to twenty-four years. There were 202 whites, 202 Negroes, and 98 Puerto Ricans. According to their maturity status, 103 subjects were in Group I, 114 in Group II, 116 in Group III, 132 in Group IV, and 37 in Group V. One single pH reading is recorded for each site of each subject; no repeat tests are listed. The readings are arranged in Table 18 according to maturity rate and test site, and Table 19 gives the corresponding means.

TABLE 18

DISTRIBUTION OF pH READINGS BY MATURITY RATE AND SKIN REGION.
502 BOYS, COLORIMETRIC MEASUREMENTS*

| Maturity Group | Skin Area Tested | Boys Tested, No. | Number of Boys in Each pH Range | | | | | | | |
|---|---|---|---|---|---|---|---|---|---|---|
| | | | 2-2.9 | 3-3.9 | 4-4.9 | 5-5.9 | 6-6.9 | 7-7.9 | 8-8.9 | 9-9.9 |
| I | Ax. vault | 103 | 0 | 9 | 73 | 18 | 3 | 0 | 0 | 0 |
| | Ax. fossa | 103 | 0 | 20 | 71 | 11 | 1 | 0 | 0 | 0 |
| | Shoulder | 89 | 10 | 42 | 33 | 4 | 0 | 0 | 0 | 0 |
| II | Ax. vault | 114 | 0 | 6 | 28 | 26 | 35 | 18 | 1 | 0 |
| | Ax. fossa | 114 | 2 | 14 | 75 | 16 | 6 | 1 | 0 | 0 |
| | Shoulder | 96 | 9 | 33 | 44 | 10 | 0 | 0 | 0 | 0 |
| III | Ax. vault | 116 | 0 | 0 | 4 | 14 | 48 | 35 | 15 | 0 |
| | Ax. fossa | 116 | 0 | 6 | 57 | 30 | 17 | 6 | 0 | 0 |
| | Shoulder | 109 | 5 | 25 | 59 | 20 | 0 | 0 | 0 | 0 |
| IV | Ax. vault | 132 | 0 | 0 | 1 | 2 | 22 | 60 | 47 | 0 |
| | Ax. fossa | 132 | 0 | 10 | 65 | 33 | 19 | 4 | 1 | 0 |
| | Shoulder | 129 | 10 | 34 | 66 | 19 | 0 | 0 | 0 | 0 |
| V | Ax. vault | 37 | 0 | 0 | 0 | 0 | 6 | 15 | 13 | 3 |
| | Ax. fossa | 37 | 0 | 2 | 14 | 13 | 7 | 1 | 0 | 0 |
| | Shoulder | 37 | 0 | 10 | 25 | 2 | 0 | 0 | 0 | 0 |

*From Behrendt and Green (8).

In the shoulder region, all values are acid in Groups I through V; most readings are below pH 5.0, and none exceeds pH 5.9.

In contrast, the mean axillary vault pH, which is acid in Group I, shows a continuous and significant shift toward alkalinity with each successive stage of maturation, reaching pH 7.6 in Group IV and pH 7.9 in Group V.

On the axillary fossa, where most sweat glands are of the eccrine type, the mean pH remains acid throughout; but there is a slight increase from one maturity group to another, with a difference of 0.9 between the means of Group I and Group V.

The dispersion of values about the means within each of the five groups deserves attention.*

The sequence of pH changes in relation to sexual development conforms to the notion that the gradual pH conversion from acid to neutral or alkaline on the axillary vault is an attribute of the activation of the apocrine sweat glands which, in turn, is a function of reproductive maturation. The axillary fossa, as one of the peripheral parts of the arm pit, participates in this increment of pH only to a minor degree, being almost void of apocrine glands. There are no group differences in the acidity of the shoulder region.

* pH readings below 3.0 and above 8.0 appear extreme; we have been unable to determine the cause for these probably false values.

TABLE 19
MEAN VALUES OF SKIN pH BY MATURITY RATES: THREE TEST AREAS,
502 BOYS, COLORIMETRIC MEAUREMENTS*

| Site | Skin pH in Each Maturity Group | | | | |
| | I | II | III | IV | V |
|---|---|---|---|---|---|
| Axillary vault | | | | | |
| Mean | 4.6 | 5.7 | 6.8 | 7.6 | 7.9 |
| S. D. | 0.56 | 1.15 | 0.93 | 0.69 | 0.71 |
| Axillary fossa | | | | | |
| Mean | 4.4 | 4.6 | 5.1 | 5.1 | 5.3 |
| S. D. | 0.56 | 0.73 | 0.89 | 0.93 | 0.93 |
| Shoulder | | | | | |
| Mean | 3.8 | 4.0 | 4.3 | 4.2 | 4.2 |
| S. D. | 0.7 | 0.76 | 0.69 | 0.82 | 0.48 |

*From Behrendt and Green (8).

## Axillary pH Patterns in Females

The 417 girls of the colorimetric series (10,11) ranged in age from one month to seventeen years. They were divided in four maturity groups (see p. 60). As to race, 204 of the females were Caucasians, 68 Negroes, and 145 Puerto Ricans. The test sites were the same as in the preceding male series. Each subject was tested once only on each of the three sites.

The sample means for each test area in each maturity group are listed in Table 20. It will be seen that the vault pH, which is strongly acid in Group I, increases with progressing maturation, reaching mean values above 7.0 in Groups III and IV. The fossa pH, which is low (4.5) in Group I, remains strongly acid in Groups II and III, but increased to 6.1 in Group IV.

The significance of the differential means has been statistically evaluated by the multiple comparison method: first, by comparing mean pH values on corresponding sites in the four groups (Table 21), and second, by comparing mean pH on the three different sites in each of the four maturity groups (Table 22).* From the analysis it becomes evident that there is a significant increase in the vault means with increasing maturation, except between Groups III and IV. For shoulder and fossa sites, the only significant increases are in Group IV. As to site means within each group, all differences are significant, except those involving the fossa in Group I and shoulder-fossa

* The t-value is a statistic which indicates the relation of the magnitude of the average difference to the chance variability of the observation. As recorded, the t-values are modified for purposes of multiple comparison. The larger the modified t-value for the same number of observations, the more significant is the average difference. We have also transformed the t-value into a statement revealing what the true average difference must at least be in order to reveal the magnitude of the actual difference obtained. We have called these least differences "lower confidence boundaries" and made these statements with the assurance that every one is correct with 98.75% confidence, i.e., on the 1.25 percent chance level.

TABLE 20
MEAN SKIN pH BY MATURITY GROUPS: THREE TEST AREAS,
357 FEMALES, COLORIMETRIC MEASUREMENTS*

| Maturity Group | Subjects in Group | Site | Skin pH | | |
| --- | --- | --- | --- | --- | --- |
| | | | Mean | ±SD | ±SE |
| I | 107 | Shoulder | 4.3 | 1.06 | 0.10 |
| | | Axillary vault | 4.8 | 1.18 | 0.11 |
| | | Axillary fossa | 4.5 | 0.94 | 0.09 |
| II | 80 | Shoulder | 4.3 | 0.60 | 0.07 |
| | | Axillary vault | 6.1 | 1.21 | 0.14 |
| | | Axillary fossa | 4.7 | 0.87 | 0.10 |
| III | 47 | Shoulder | 4.3 | 0.79 | 0.12 |
| | | Axillary vault | 7.5 | 0.78 | 0.11 |
| | | Axillary fossa | 4.9 | 1.05 | 0.15 |
| IV | 123 | Shoulder | 5.1 | 0.79 | 0.07 |
| | | Axillary vault | 7.1 | 0.67 | 0.06 |
| | | Axillary fossa | 6.1 | 1.14 | 0.10 |

*From Behrendt et al. (11).

TABLE 21
COMPARISON OF MEAN pH ON CORRESPONDING SITES IN FOUR
MATURITY GROUPS: 357 FEMALES, COLORIMETRIC READINGS*

| Site | Maturity Groups Compared | Mean pH Differences | Modified t | Lower Confidence Boundary |
| --- | --- | --- | --- | --- |
| Shoulder | I & II | 0 | —— | —— |
| | I & III | 0 | —— | —— |
| | I & IV | 0.8 | 6.12 | 0.31 |
| | II & III | 0 | —— | —— |
| | II & IV | 0.8 | 6.56 | 0.27 |
| | III & IV | 0.8 | 5.49 | 0.16 |
| Axillary fossa | I & II | 0.2 | 1.33 | —— |
| | I & III | 0.4 | 2.12 | —— |
| | I & IV | 0.6 | 11.97 | 0.01 |
| | II & III | 0.2 | 1.07 | —— |
| | II & IV | 1.4 | 9.57 | 0.76 |
| | III & IV | 1.2 | 6.87 | 0.44 |
| Axillary vault | I & II | 1.3 | 8.84 | 0.66 |
| | I & III | 2.7 | 15.51 | 1.94 |
| | I & IV | 2.3 | 17.50 | 1.73 |
| | II & III | 1.4 | 7.64 | 0.60 |
| | II & IV | 1.0 | 7.00 | 0.38 |
| | III & IV | 0.4 | 2.34 | —— |

Critical value of t: 4.36 (1.25% level, single tail).
*From Behrendt et al. (11).

TABLE 22

COMPARISON OF MEAN pH ON THREE DIFFERENT SITES IN EACH OF FOUR
MATURITY GROUPS: 357 FEMALES, COLORIMETRIC READINGS*

| Maturity Group | Sites Compared | Mean pH Differences | Modified t | Lower Confidence Boundary |
|---|---|---|---|---|
| I | Shoulder & fossa | 0.2 | 2.11 | .... |
| I | Shoulder & vault | 0.5 | 5.32 | 0.09 |
| I | Fossa & vault | 0.3 | 1.56 | .... |
| II | Shoulder & fossa | 0.4 | 3.62 | .... |
| II | Shoulder & vault | 1.8 | 16.42 | 1.32 |
| II | Fossa & vault | 1.4 | 9.66 | 0.77 |
| III | Shoulder & fossa | 0.6 | 4.19 | .... |
| III | Shoulder & vault | 3.2 | 22.51 | 2.58 |
| III | Fossa & vault | 2.6 | 9.23 | 1.38 |
| IV | Shoulder & fossa | 1.0 | 11.23 | 0.61 |
| IV | Shoulder & vault | 2.0 | 22.62 | 1.62 |
| IV | Fossa & vault | 1.0 | 5.73 | 0.24 |

Critical value of t: 4.36 (1.25% level, single tail).
*From Behrendt et al. (11).

TABLE 23

SKIN pH ON THREE AXILLARY SITES AND SHOULDER OF ADOLESCENT
GIRLS*

| | | SKIN pH | | |
|---|---|---|---|---|
| | | | Axillary Fossa | |
| No. | Axillary Vault | Groove | Periphery | Shoulder |
| H34 | 7.2 | 6.7 | 6.0 | 5.0 |
| H35 | 7.6 | 7.2 | 7.0 | 4.3 |
| H38 | 7.3 | 6.7 | 4.8 | 5.2 |
| H60 | 7.7 | 7.1 | 5.4 | 5.4 |
| H61 | 7.4 | 7.0 | 5.0 | 5.2 |
| H62 | 7.3 | 7.3 | 5.3 | 4.4 |
| H65 | 7.5 | 7.4 | 6.9 | 4.8 |
| H72 | 7.1 | 6.8 | 6.0 | .... |

*From Behrendt et al. (11). Colorimetric readings.

differences in Groups II and III (although the latter is significant on the 5%
level).

In an attempt to clarify the participation of the fossa in the alkalinization
of the axillary space in the girls of Group IV, we tested eight subjects of this
group on a site outside of the fossa, i.e., in an area 1 to 2 cm beyond the
anatomic confines of the fossa's groove. As shown in Table 23, in seven of the
eight girls we found the alkaline zone to reach from the vault into the con-
tiguous superior part of the fossa and into the central groove. However, at the
periphery of the fossa (in posterior, anterior , and caudal direction) the pH
was distinctly lower, often markedly acid.

We conclude that the moderate pH increase in the fossa and the pH rise on the vault of female adolescents have a different origin. The latter is the result of an intrinsic process, while the former is most likely, due to an overflow of apocrine sweat from the vault. In the absence of a converted "alkaline" vault pH, increases of the fossa pH have not been found to approach neutral values. As in boys, the rise of the vault pH in adolescent girls is a function of activation of the a-glands.

Measurements with the glass electrode were made on an additional 60 girls of Group IV. As shown in Figure 14 and Table 24, the results confirm

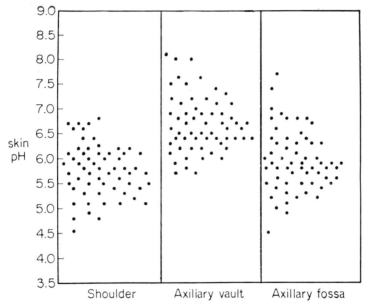

FIGURE 14. Scattergram showing potentiometric pH readings on three skin areas in 60 girls of Group IV. Means (±SD): on *shoulder*, pH 5.7 (±0.54); on *vault*, pH 6.7 (±0.56); on *fossa*, pH (±0.61). From Behrendt *et al.* (11). (Reproduced with permission of *Amer J. Dis. Child.*)

TABLE 24
SKIN pH: THREE SITES IN SIXTY GIRLS OF GROUP IV.
POTENTIOMETRIC MEASUREMENTS*

| Site | Mean pH | S.D. | Sites Compared | Mean pH Differences | Modified t | Lower Confidence Boundary |
|---|---|---|---|---|---|---|
| Shoulder | 5.7 ± | 0.54 | Shoulder & fossa | 0.2 | 3.77 | 0.03 |
| Fossa | 5.9 | 0.61 | Shoulder & vault | 1.0 | 22.47 | 0.86 |
| Vault | 6.7 | 0.56 | Fossa & vault | 0.8 | 17.77 | 0.66 |

Critical value of t: 3.17 (1.25% level, single tail).
*From Behrendt et al. (11).

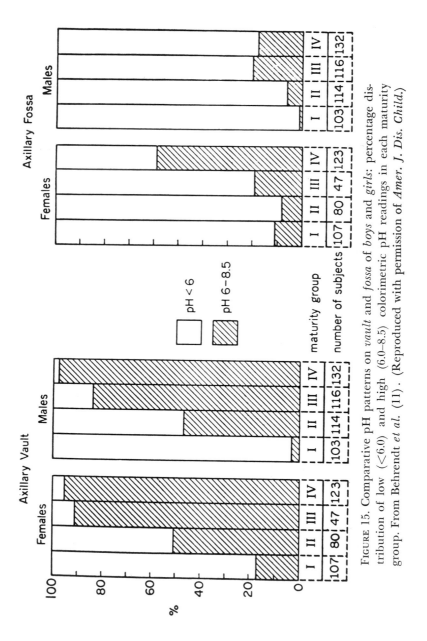

FIGURE 15. Comparative pH patterns on *vault* and *fossa* of *boys* and *girls*: percentage distribution of low (<6.0) and high (6.0–8.5) colorimetric pH readings in each maturity group. From Behrendt *et al.* (11). (Reproduced with permission of *Amer. J. Dis. Child.*)

the trend of pH changes as established by colorimetric measurements. The mean vault readings exceed the means for fossa and shoulder significantly. Most readings on the vault fall between pH 6 and 8, while values below 6.5 predominate on shoulder and fossa. The results are illustrative of the outcome of comparative serial measurements performed with the electrode and indicator, respectively. Although absolute values differ considerably, the same trend of pH changes is revealed by either method of determination.

The foregoing data provide evidence that pH conversion on the axillary vault follows the same pattern in both sexes. However, the analogy is not complete. As illustrated in Figure 15, the proportion of girls in whom the pH shift precedes the appearance of any secondary sex character is higher than that of boys: 18% of the females in Group I, against 4% of the males in Group I. These data suggest that apocrine gland function starts indeed earlier in girls than in boys, as claimed in the literature. In Group IV, a still higher proportion of girls than boys show fossa pH readings above 6.0: 60% and 19%, respectively. As stated above, the reason for this higher incidence is not directly related to maturation but is of extrinsic nature.

## pH CHANGES ON OPEN SKIN SURFACES

We will now resume the discussion of skin acidity on exposed surfaces and follow its course from school age through the ensuing periods of development. Most published data conform to the notion that average skin acidity remains relatively stationary throughout late childhood, preadolescence, adolescence, and adulthood. This is borne out by:

1. the data listed for children in the preceding chapter;
2. our findings for the various age groups between 2 and 15 years, as illustrated in Figure 11; and
3. Arbenz's scattergram reproduced in Figure 16, demonstrating that the mean pH level on open surfaces "remains static throughout life."

A deviation from this continuous course has been detected by Blank (17), who compared the surface pH on the arms of 3- to 14-year-old children with that of adults. While his data, reproduced in Table 25, confirm the close similarity between pH levels of female children and female adults, the recorded mean values for male adults are consistently more acid than those for male children. In either age group, the means for females exceed those for males.

It is difficult to accept these findings as evidence that the surface pH on the arms of boys decreases "after puberty", i.e., as an attribute of adolescence. If such a conclusion were correct, pH measurements on subjects of different maturity should reveal a trend of the pH to rise with each successive stage of development. This is not the case as evidenced by our data on boys of differ-

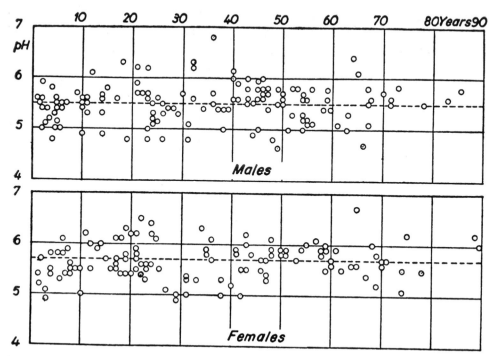

FIGURE 16. Scattergram showing potentiometric pH readings on the chest in relation to *nine* decades of age. Upper part, *males*; lower part, *females*. From Arbenz (3). (Reproduced with permission of the author and *Dermatologica*.)

TABLE 25

**SUBJECT MEANS FOR ARM SURFACE pH, SIX SITES, IN CHILDREN AND ADULTS, POTENTIOMETRIC MEASUREMENTS***

| | MEAN SKIN pH | | | |
| Site | Children | | Adults | |
| | 100 Males | 100 Females | 100 Males | 100 Females |
|---|---|---|---|---|
| Forearm, flexor surface | 4.87 | 5.11 | 4.45 | 5.15 |
| Forearm, extensor surface | 4.97 | 5.33 | 4.56 | 5.33 |
| Antecubital fossa | 4.62 | 4.82 | 4.37 | 4.80 |
| Elbow point | 4.97 | 5.11 | 4.64 | 5.20 |
| Upper arm, flexor surface | 4.73 | 4.97 | 4.58 | 5.11 |
| Upper arm, extensor surface | 4.88 | 5.16 | 4.67 | 5.26 |

*From Blank (17).

ent maturity rating: their mean skin acidity on the shoulder remained unchanged from childhood through all stages of adolescence (Table 19). In our studies on females, however, the shoulder pH maintained the same level only through the first 3 phases of maturation; in girls of Group IV, the mean acidity declined by 0.8 pH unit (Tables 20 and 21). Thus we found not only that a maturity-dependent pH shift on "eccrine" areas occurs in girls solely, but that this shift takes the opposite direction as in Blank's male subjects.

That such shifts in pH should be restricted to girls will fit into the commonly held belief that the pH of the acid mantle is slightly higher in adult females than in adult males (16,42,121,148). Only a few data are available regarding the influence of sex on the pH of open surfaces in infants and children. During the newborn period, as we have seen, no sex-dependent pH differences could be demonstrated with certainty in full-term infants, while in low-birth-weight infants sex was shown to be a significant variant, effecting higher means in females than males. From all other information it can be intimated that the pH on eccrine surfaces tends to be higher in female than in male children and preadolescents, if a difference is detectable at all. Are such differences related to the well-known fact that women have a lower sweating capacity than men?

## PHYSIOLOGIC CORRELATIONS

Our pH studies have established the trend of vault pH readings to increase with the ongoing development of secondary sex characters. One may qualify these pH changes as a chemical sign of sexual maturation. The apocrine sweat glands responsible for the pH conversion can be said to behave like a secondary sex character, an epithet suggested by Bunting *et al* (22) to describe the close relation between the morphologic maturation of a-glands and the appearance of the various external signs of sexual growth.

There are other growth-related changes which reflected not simply the length of time a child has lived, but are indicative of the attained progress towards sexual maturity. For instance, skeletal age is closely related to sexual development (57). "Normals" for concentration of many constituents of body fluids show age-dependent alterations mainly during the transition from intrauterine to extrauterine life and from childhood to adolescence. In this section we will discuss how pH conversion on the vault relates to some of the other attributes of reproductive growth.

### pH Changes on Axillary Vault and Vaginal Mucosa

On each of these surfaces, pH conversion takes place concomitantly three times during life, each time in opposite direction. In the newly born infant the entire skin surface, including the axilla, is of uniformly neutral or alkaline reaction. This high pH is converted to markedly acid values during the postnatal period. In contrast, the vaginal surface is strongly acid on the first few days after birth and undergoes alkalinization during the following weeks. With onset of adolescence, when the vault pH is shifting from the puerile acid reaction to or above neutrality, the heretofore alkaline vaginal pH turns acid again and remains acid throughout the period of reproductive capacity. With sexual involution, the vaginal pH reverts to alkalinity, while the axillary vault pH declines to acid values. These changes are illustrated in Figure 17.

In the vagina, these three pH conversions are due to changes in circulating estrogen concentrations and concurrent transformations of the vaginal epithelium (40,49,146,147).

In the newborn infant, the vaginal mucosa is of the mature, estrogen-stimulated type, characterized by a stratified squamous epithelium, more than 15 layers deep. Some of the cells are cornified; oval and round elements of the middle layers contain large deposits of glycogen. Mucosal surface and the copious secretions are of strongly acid reactions (around pH 5.5). Acidification takes place inside the epithelial cells and is due to enzymatic formation of lactic acid from glycogen; bacterial action is not involved. These features develop during the last 3 fetal months under the stimulus of maternal estrogens which increase continuously during gestation and pass into the fetal circulation. At the time of delivery, the plasma levels of estrogen vary within equally high ranges (10–80 μg/100ml) in mother and child (39). During the last weeks of pregnancy, maternal estrogen excretion in the urine is somewhere between 15,300 and 22,400 μg per day; the neonate excretes from 500 to 1,500 μg per day (50).

After birth, the neonate's vaginal mucosa is gradually transformed into the infantile, quiescent type, when maternal estrogens are rapidly excreted and the child's own production of estrogens is negligible. On the tenth day after birth, the infant's urinary estrogen excretion drops to an average of 1–2 μg/24 hr (50), and towards

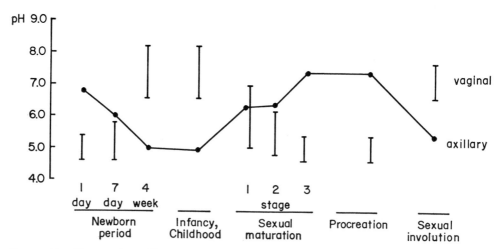

FIGURE 17. Changes in *axillary* vault pH (mean values) and *vaginal* mucosal pH (ranges) from birth through old age. Based on data of literature.

the end of the first month of life, the infant's vaginal mucosa looks inert, almost atrophic, consisting of a few layers of epithelial cells which are nearly devoid of glycogen. Mucosal surface pH and the scanty secretions show a neutral or alkaline reaction.

These inert, infantile features persist throughout childhood, with urinary estrogen excretion varying from 0 to 3.5 $\mu g/24$ hr (39). However, with onset of adolescence and the concurrent increase in estrogen production, the vaginal epithelium is transformed into the mature, hypertrophic state, and the vaginal surface turns acid. The mucosa retains these estrogen-stimulated characteristics throughout the period of reproductive capacity with urinary estrogen excretion rates of 10 to 40 $\mu g/day$ (39). When menopause sets in, the ovary becomes unresponsive to gonadotropic stimulation, estrogen production declines, and vaginal mucosa reverts gradually to the atrophic state, with mucosal pH values turning neutral again.

The changes in axillary skin pH of the female, though almost coinciding with the opposite pH changes on the vaginal mucosa, are not related to estrogen production. During the newborn period, the reversal of the vault pH from neutral to acid is probably of extrinsic and not of endocrine nature. This acidification involves the entire body surface. However, the shift of the vault pH from acid to neutral values at the beginning of adolescence and the reverse changes with onset of sexual involution must be related to endocrine factors, although their nature is still unknown.

## Vault pH, Sexual Maturation, and Sex Hormone Activity

When Greulich established the close relationship between the anatomic development of a-glands and of external sex characters, he also presented suggestive evidence that structural a-gland development paralleled the gradual unfolding of sex hormone activity, as measured by urinary excretion rates of estrogenic, androgenic, and gonadotropic substances. How specific hormonal activities relate to maturity rating, has not yet been established, insofar as we are aware. Similarly, a-gland activation and conversion of vault pH in relation to specific sex hormone production has yet to be defined. Circumstantial evidence remains ambiguous. For instance, since estrogens are known to have a depressing effect on the proliferation of apocrine sweat glands (33, 111) and on the development of sebaceous glands (44), Rothman (116a) has suggested that the two kinds of glands may also be activated by the same hormonal factors.* On the other hand, mammary and apocrine glands seem to be controlled by a common hormonal principle; they have long been known to undergo development as well as involutionary changes in close parallelism. Estrogen activity is considered likely to exert such a common control.

Similar deductions with regard to androgenic action on apocrine glands in

---

* Activation of sebaceous glands is effected by testicular hormone in the male (54, 59) and by progesterone in the female (113). There is an antagonism between androgens and estrogens with respect to their action on sebaceous glands (134).

males have been made from a comparison with those secondary sex characters whose appearance coincides with a-gland activation. Such attempts must fail as long as the endocrine principles responsible for the growth of each individual sex character are undefined.

## Reversal of Vault pH During Sexual Involution

We have extended the study of pH changes to the period of sexual involution. One may expect a reversal of the vault pH to acid values when apocrine sweat secretion ceases as the result of regression and atrophy of a-glands in old age (33, 103). The only previous measurements on old people we are aware of are reported in a study of Arbenz (3). He found the mean pH values on chest and forehead of elderly people to be similar to those of children and of adults below 60 years. The axillary pH, however, was distinctly lower in persons over 60 years than in those between 15 and 60 years of age.

Our data were collected from eighty-one individuals, from 54 to 97 years of age. While all females were allegedly in the menopause, there was no feasible way of assessing the reproductive capacity of males. Hence the readings had to be arranged according to age. Although the number in each age group was small and disparate, the results as listed in Table 26 and 27 can leave no doubt that the high pH on the axillary vault is no longer present in old age. Only 12 of 81 vault readings exceed pH 5.9. In 54- to 70-year-old subjects, the means for the vault pH, though below 6.0, are still higher than in persons over 70 years old. This may be interpreted as an indication that some a-glands remain operative until the end of the seventh decade of life, in either sex.* Indeed, the few males with vault readings exceeding pH 6.9 (Table 26) were all between 57 and 63 years, while three among the five

TABLE 26
DISTRIBUTION OF COLORIMETRIC pH READINGS BY SEX AND SITE IN EIGHTY-ONE SUBJECTS AGED FIFTY-FOUR TO NINETY-SEVEN YEARS

| Subjects[1] | Test Site | No. of Readings in Each pH Range | | | | |
|---|---|---|---|---|---|---|
| | | <4 | 4.0-4.9 | 5.0-5.9 | 6.0-6.9 | 7.0-7.9 |
| 28 Males | Axill. vault | 11 | 6 | 4 | 3 | 4 |
| | Axill. fossa | 16 | 9 | 1 | 2 | — |
| | Shoulder | 25 | 3 | — | — | — |
| 53 Females | Axill. vault | 15 | 25 | 8 | 1 | 4 |
| | Axill. fossa | 25 | 21 | 6 | — | 1 |
| | Shoulder | 36 | 14 | 3 | — | — |

[1]Distribution by age is given in Table 27.

* The aging changes in a-gland morphology have been described as not peremptory, some glandular units showing atrophy and mucoid metaplasia, others not (44c). The lack of uniformity in axillary pH conversion among persons of old age would be the functional equivalent of the differential structural changes.

females with such high readings were even older than 77 years. One of them, at the age of 83, having been in the menopause for 20 years, had a pungent apocrine smell emanating from the axillae. Arbenz (3) was inclined to infer similar sex differences from his data.

The mean pH levels on the axillary fossa are, throughout, lower than on the vault and higher than on the shoulder; in males, the fossa means decline from pH 4.8 (in the lower age group) to 3.5 (in the oldest group). The strong acidity on the shoulder site shows little variation from one age period to another.

TABLE 27

MEAN SKIN pH ON THREE TEST SITES OF EIGHTY-ONE ELDERLY
SUBJECTS BY AGE GROUPS (COLORIMETRIC READINGS)

| Age, Sex | No. of Subjects | Vault | | Fossa | | Shoulder | |
|---|---|---|---|---|---|---|---|
| | | Mean pH | S.D. | Mean pH | S.D. | Mean pH | S.D. |
| 54-60 yrs. | | | | | | | |
| Males | 7 | 5.58 | ±1.87 | 4.80 | ±1.21 | 3.44 | ±0.33 |
| Females | 6 | 5.22 | 1.36 | 4.12 | 0.48 | 3.20 | 0.42 |
| 61-70 yrs. | | | | | | | |
| Males | 7 | 5.14 | 1.32 | 4.10 | 0.94 | 3.14 | 0.36 |
| Females | 6 | 4.70 | 0.74 | 4.63 | 0.85 | 3.65 | 0.94 |
| 71-80 yrs. | | | | | | | |
| Males | 9 | 4.20 | 1.03 | 3.62 | 0.70 | 3.46 | 0.62 |
| Females | 21 | 4.44 | 0.80 | 4.18 | 0.79 | 3.64 | 0.62 |
| 81-97 yrs. | | | | | | | |
| Males | 5 | 4.09 | 10.6 | 3.50 | 0.44 | 3.22 | 0.37 |
| Females | 20 | 4.37 | 1.12 | 4.16 | 0.95 | 3.84 | 0.67 |
| 61-97 yrs. | | | | | | | |
| Males | 21 | 4.49 | 1.37 | 3.75 | 0.82 | 3.30 | 0.51 |
| Females | 47 | 4.45 | 0.94 | 4.23 | 0.88 | 3.73 | 0.70 |

TABLE 28

MEAN SKIN pH ON THREE SITES IN RELATION TO REPRODUCTIVE
CAPACITY

| Site and Sex | Pre-adolescence [1] | | Late Adolescence [2] | | Sexual Involution [3] | |
|---|---|---|---|---|---|---|
| | Mean pH | S.D. | Mean pH | S.D. | Mean pH | S.D. |
| Shoulder | | | | | | |
| Males | 3.8 ± | 0.70 | 4.2 ± | 0.82 | 3.3 ± | 0.51 |
| Females | 4.3 | 1.06 | 5.1 | 0.79 | 3.7 | 0.70 |
| Axill. fossa | | | | | | |
| Males | 4.4 | 0.56 | 5.1 | 0.93 | 3.8 | 0.82 |
| Females | 4.5 | 0.94 | 6.1 | 1.14 | 4.2 | 0.88 |
| Axill. vault | | | | | | |
| Males | 4.6 | 0.56 | 7.6 | 0.69 | 4.5 | 1.37 |
| Females | 4.8 | 1.18 | 7.1 | 0.67 | 4.5 | 0.94 |

[1]Maturity Group I, Table 19 and 20.   [2]Maturity Group IV, Table 19 and 20.   [3] 21 males, 47 females over 60 years of age.

The site means calculated for females plus males, but exclusive of the subjects between 54 and 60 years, are probably most representative of the pH pattern prevailing during old age. These means have been inserted in Table 28 to show the contrast between levels associated with preadolescence, reproductive maturity, and sexual involution.

# Chapter VIII

# USE OF THE AXILLARY pH TEST IN THE APPRAISAL OF ADOLESCENT DEVELOPMENT

Conversion of the vault pH occurs eventually in every healthy boy and girl, but the developmental age at which the pH change takes place varies considerably among individuals of both sexes. As we have seen, there are subjects with converted and unconverted pH values to be found among adolescents of any developmental class; only the proportion of converted to total readings increases with maturation, and likewise the mean vault pH of each successive maturity group. Clearly, these mean values cannot be used as criteria for evaluating individual vault readings as normal or abnormal with respect to the subject's maturity rating.

Still, we have found over the years that under certain conditions, determination of the vault pH may be equally or more informative than the relative development attained by secondary sex characters. The basis for using this additional criterion is provided by the frequency distribution of converted vault readings in the various maturity groups. As evidenced in Figure 15, the pH conversion is an early sign of sexual development; it takes place prior to the appearance of secondary sex characters in 10% of all children and can be demonstrated in every second boy or girl while they are still in the first stage of sexual maturation, i.e., in Group II according to our rating. This permits one to establish the presence of a chemical sign at a time when somatic changes may be still missing.

Production of a-gland-stimulating hormone is reflected by the result of the axillary pH test in a similar way as estrogenic activity by the outcome of the vaginal pH test with nitrazin paper (146).

## PROCEDURE

As a clinical test, axillary pH measurement is carried out preferably with the indicator method, for three reasons: (a) because basic data on physiologic pH conversion on the vault have been largely obtained by means of the colorimetric method; (b) because the pH shift is magnified and easier defined when measured with the indicator than with the electrode; and (c) because of the inexpensiveness of testing material and the easy application of the indicator method in office practice, where potentiometric equipment is not readily available.

Measurements are taken on vault and fossa of the axilla and at the shoulder site, as described previously. No cosmetics should be used on the test sites within 24 hours prior to the testing. The sites should not be cleansed before the drop of indicator solution is applied, even when perspiration is marked.

The pH values as read from the color chart are differentiated as follows:

below pH 6.0 = puerile readings
between pH 6.0 and 6.5 = intermediate readings
above pH 6.5 = "green" or adolescent readings

In this way, ranges rather than values are distinguished, to conform to the method's limited reproducibility and to avoid pseudoaccuracy.

Generally, shoulder readings will be more or less acid (pH<6.0) ; if they are not, the reaction is probably "false" and a control measurement is made on the contralateral shoulder site. If the reading turns out to be equally high, testing is discontinued and repeated on another day. Although such experiences are rare, they warrant th performance of the shoulder test as a routine control.

On the vault, intermediate readings indicate that no conclusions can be drawn as to the functional state of the apocrine glands, and that the test should be repeated in a few weeks. "Green" readings on the vault signify that pH conversion has taken place and the hormonal changes of adolescence are under way. The relative "alkalinity" of the pH value has no clinical significance. Vault readings below pH 6.0 indicate that hormonal induction of a-gland activity has not yet taken place.

Readings on the axillary fossa are actually dispensible, but are customarily taken to define the extent to which fossa pH has increased by the overflow of apocrine sweat from the adjacent vault.

## APPLICATIONS

We have used the test extensively in the periodic follow-up of preadolescents. In healthy boys or girls whose sexual development proceeds according to normal patterns, the vault pH will undergo conversion at some time or another during maturation, more frequently during the early stages. The time at which this may happen is not predictable and has probably no clinical significance, as long as the development of secondary sex characters conforms to normally increasing production of sex hormones.

The physician will also observe with interest how conversion of vault pH and secondary sex characters develop concurrently in cases of precocious maturation, both of the constitutional and pathologic variety. A second or third grader, who stands out among his classmates because of his accelerated sexual growth, will rarely fail to have a converted vault pH. Similarly, a 6-year-old boy, who was referred to us because of rapid sexual maturation and other symptoms of the Cushing Syndrome, had a converted vault pH of 7.6. His pathology was confirmed as adrenal hyperplasia. In another instance, a $4\frac{1}{2}$-year-old girl, with manifestations of precocious sexual maturation was found to have a converted axillary pH of 7.3; the patient was signed out before the diagnosis could be established. It would be of great interest to know how vault pH is affected by selective premature development of sexual hair (pubarche) or breasts (thelarche).

The test becomes diagnostically more meaningful in the appraisal of individuals with unusally delayed sexual maturation. If periodic check-ups fail to show progress in sexual growth, determination of the vault pH may reveal conversion to adolescent values and thus mark the impending appearance of somatic changes. We have never encountered an axillary pH conversion which was not followed by noticeable somatic development within a short time, often within a matter of weeks. Clearly, in such cases of idiopathic delay of maturation the outcome of the axillary pH test will influence judgment as to whether steps should be taken to define the etiology of the presumed developmental disorder. We do not have sufficient data to indicate whether the rates of urinary androgen or estrogen excretion show an equally conclusive increase at the time when pH conversion occurs. An example may illustrate how the test may serve the stated objective.

A 14-year-old boy was referred because of failure to develop sexually. He had neither pubic, axillary or facial hair, nor acne. His testes and scrotum were entirely infantile. His height-age was 8.5 years, his bone-age 12 years. Urinary 17-ketosteroid excretion was 2.6 mg/24 hr. He had received no therapy of any kind. However, the vault pH was found to be 7.5, a clearly converted value. Based on these data, the condition was judged to be the result of delayed adolescence. That some stimulating endocrine activity was already at work was suggested by the relatively advanced bone age and the pH conversion on the vault. It would have been justified to anticipate spontaneous progress in sexual growth and to forgo any treatment. For psychologic reasons however, a single course of hormone therapy with chorionic gonadotropin was instituted and resulted in the desired rapid development of some virile features, replacing the stigma of infantilism. One year later, without any further stimulation, sexual maturation continued at a normal pace.

Less frequently, development of secondary sex characters as well as vault pH conversion will remain conspicuously absent for a time span exceeding by far the physiologic limits. This should be a signal for initiating the diagnostic measures required for proper management. If the condition is one of endocrine deficiency and substitution therapy is instituted, the subsequent responses of target organs will include the pH conversion on the vault. Again, there will be the opportunity to observe the relation between a-gland activation and growth of sex characters.

A case in question is a 14-year-old boy whom we guided through the difficult years of an endocrine pathology caused by pituitary gonadotropic deficiency. In the presence of sexual infantilism, linear and osseous growth proceeded at normal rates. It took two years of exploration to establish the diagnosis and a sound basis for initiating substitution therapy.

Prior to treatment, axillary vault pH was found repeatedly to be strongly acid. At the age of almost 17 years, after four months of continual testosterone therapy, there was a remarkable increase in the growth of sexual hair and sex organs—and the vault pH had converted to 7.5.

*Summary.* pH conversion on the vault is a chemical sign indicating the onset of a-gland function. By visualizing this conversion, the axillary pH test extends the examination for sexual development to another target organ of sex hormones. Measurement of the vault pH is of both physiologic and clinical interest and is of particular value in the appraisal of delayed onset of adolescence.

# Chapter IX

# PATHOLOGIC CHANGES IN SURFACE pH

T he "abnormalities" mentioned in the preceding chapter consist of pH changes which are unusual only in so far as they occur at an excessively early or late stage of development. The following discussion deals with some of the few occasions at which the surface pH itself tends to be excessively low or high as compared to average normal levels. A genuinely abnormal pH pattern is rare; it may be due to pathology of or trauma to the skin. The more frequently found abnormalities in skin pH are those induced by a variety of contactants commonly used as skin cleansers and baby toiletries. (See chapter X).

## SURFACE pH AND SKIN DISEASE

Indications are that the direction of a pH shift on diseased skin areas depends on the nature of the lesion. Desquamation, lichenification, atrophy, and pyogenic infection are known to result in slight increases or no change in acidity (78), while many forms of dermatitis effect a pH shift towards alkalinity. A close-to-neutral surface reaction will be found in the presence of serous fluid. Fluid from blisters caused by infection has a pH around 7.0, while vesicles of dyshidrosis due to sweat retention contain a strongly acid fluid (85).

In some instances, obvious pathologic processes, like inflammation and exudation, cause no significant pH changes, for reasons still unknown. Since many skin disorders show a combination of different pathologic processes, a correlation between pH readings and specific types of morphologic lesions is often difficult to establish. Furthermore, it has been shown that children with certain skin diseases have altered pH levels not only at the sites of morphologic pathology, but also on unaffected surfaces.

### Microsporon Infection of Scalp

Herrmann *et al.* (62) examined 142 patients with tinea capitis, caused by *Microsporum audouini*. Surface pH was measured colorimetrically on the affected scalp areas, on apparently healthy areas of the scalp, and at several skin sites of chest and extremities. Comparative measurements were made on the corresponding sites of eighty-seven healthy children of similar age. The results disclose the following differential pH patterns:

Prior to institution of therapy, readings on the diseased scalp areas are

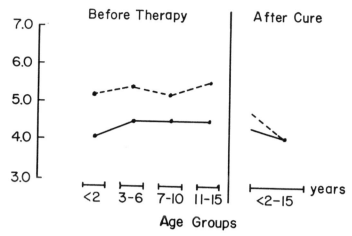

FIGURE 18. Colorimetric pH measurements in 142 children with Microsporon infection of the scalp. Means for normal (*solid line*) and infected areas (*dotted lines*) of the scalp, *before treatment* and *after cure*. Drawn from data of Herrmann *et al.* (62) .

consistently and distinctly higher than those on the unaffected parts of the scalp. Figure 18 illustrates these differences, which amount to at least 0.5 pH unit in all age groups. Although no statistic evaluation was attempted, the number of test subjects was large enough to suggest that these differences are no chance-findings. This belief is supported by the fact that measurements on the same patients after they had been cured showed the scalp pH on the same infected areas to have declined to the means of the unaffected sites of the scalp; the differences in pH had disappeared completely.

The following conclusions were drawn from these observations: (a) The increase in surface pH on the scalp lesions must be regarded as due to a non-specific, acidity-lowering effect of inflammatory changes. (b) There is no conclusive evidence that a constitutional factor causing lowered skin acidity is responsible for a predisposition of some children to infection with the microsporon. (c) The relationship, if any, between changes in skin properties incident to adolescence on one hand, and the restriction of tinea capitis to preadolescent children on the other hand, remains to be defined.

### Seborrheic Dermatitis

Seborrheic dermatitis has been chosen by some workers as the model for studying the relation of surface pH to particular types of skin lesions.

In the first of such studies carried out with the glass electrode, Anderson (2) compared the average pH for corresponding sites in 50 healthy children and 50 children with seborrheic eczema. In both groups the age of the subjects ranged from one month to 12 years. The results are listed in Table 29, which clearly shows the mean pH to be higher in the affected than in the

TABLE 29
MEAN SURFACE pH ON CORRESPONDING SITES IN HEALTHY CHILDREN
AND CHILDREN WITH SEBORRHEIC DERMATITIS*

| Site | Normal | | Seborrheic | |
|------|--------|--------|--------|--------|
| | No. Tested | Mean pH | No. Tested | Mean pH |
| Dorsum hand | 37 | 5.04 | 8 | 5.71 |
| Palm hand | 33 | 5.25 | 9 | 5.77 |
| Wrist flex. surf. | 23 | 5.33 | 9 | 5.74 |
| Antecubit. fossa | 22 | 5.44 | 9 | 6.24 |
| Axilla | 7 | 5.45 | 6 | 6.33 |
| Cheek | 22 | 5.28 | 10 | 6.42 |
| Scalp | 10 | 5.00 | 4 | 6.45 |
| Retroauric. fold | 3 | 4.87 | 5 | 6.28 |
| Sole foot | 8 | 5.25 | 3 | 5.47 |
| Popliteal fossa | 19 | 5.53 | 9 | 6.48 |

*According to Anderson (2).

healthy children, on all ten test sites. The means range from 5.04 to 5.53 in the healthy subjects, and from 5.71 to 6.48 in the seborrheic group.

In individual cases the skin pH was found at levels occurring physiologically only on apocrine skin areas. In a 4-month-old boy, for instance, who had acute weeping, and crusted lesions on face and scalp, and additional subacute lesions on hands, arms and popliteal fossae, the following readings were recorded:

| | Patient | Healthy Boy of Same Age |
|------|--------|--------|
| face (right) | pH 7.8 | pH 4.7 |
| face (left) | 7.7 | — |
| forehead | 7.9 | 4.8 |
| poplitea (right) | 7.6 | 5.7 |
| wrist (right) | 6.5 | 5.4 |

What is most remarkable in Anderson's findings is the general rise in pH over the whole body surface, i.e., on affected and unaffected skin areas of seborrheic children. This suggests that a constitutional factor may be in part responsible for the changed properties of the skin in seborrheic subjects, even in the absence of actual lesions.

Another finding of Anderson concerns the pH on dry or xerodermatic skin in Besnier's prurigo (atopic dermatitis). In the presence of xeroderma, the pH also tends to be raised over the whole body surface, although not to the same degree as in seborrheic dermatitis.

Beare *et al.* (4) corroborated the results of Anderson in seborrheic dermatitis in a study of children aged 3 months to 3 years. Using the glass electrode and comparing the pH on 16 corresponding sites, they found the site means in 45 affected children to be 0.3 to 0.5 pH unit higher than in 45 healthy children. The authors conclude that seborrhea makes the skin pH more alkaline even in the absence of clinical manifestations. Seborrheic lesions are said to be a reflection of a constitutional disorder. One will be reminded at once of two other attributes of the eczematous and seborrheic skin: its diminished alkali-resistance (25) and increased acid-resistance (120, 124).

## Burns

Epidermal surface and barrier zone, the sites of skin acidification, are no longer fully operative even in minor injuries caused by heat. Burns of various gradations will therefore differ only in the degree to which acidity is reduced below its normal range. On lesions exposing deeper epidermal strata or the corium, the surface pH will reflect the alkaline reaction of these layers. Tissue debris, exudation, and topical treatment will influence the surface reaction in varying degrees.

Measurements made on two pediatric patients may illustrate the pH pattern to be found on burned skin surfaces.

### Case 1

A 6-year-old girl was tested immediately after being admitted because of burns suffered 4 days previously and not yet treated. The lesions were considered to be of second-to-third degree, extending over most of the abdominal wall below the navel. The injured area showed a combination of blisters, moist portions, jelly like-debris, and dry crusted lesions, with erythema on the circumference. Potentiometric readings were as follows:

pH 7.5—on the areas of deepest destruction (dry)
pH 6.8—on the moist sites
pH 6.2—on the erythematous borders
pH 5.5—on intact, neighboring surfaces

### Case 2

This 7-month-old girl was tested thirteen days after she had suffered a second-degree burn on the flexor surface of upper thigh and adjacent buttock. She was treated by the "open method," the injured area being loosely covered with mesh gauze, which was kept wet-soaked by a solution of bacitracin in saline dropping continuously from a container onto the gauze cover. The solution had a pH of 6.4. For the test this treatment was interrupted, the gauze removed, and the electrodes placed on the exposed, moist, red-mottled, debris-free surface. Readings were as follows:

pH 8.1—on all parts of the burned area
pH 6.3—on the adjacent uninjured sites of the buttock
pH 6.1—on the healthy skin of the contralateral buttock site

The prolonged application of the weakly acid bacitracin solution had, apparently, not influenced the surface pH of the exposed skin layers.

## SURFACE pH ON ANHIDROTIC SKIN AREAS

If the peripheral pathways of the thermal sweating reflex are damaged or interrupted, partial or total anhidrosis may result in the areas of distribution of the injured neurons. Delineation of such anhidrotic areas has been used in the evaluation of nerve injuries and in the study of recovery of neuronal function, especially after nerve suture and skin grafting.

Unlike examination for sensory loss, testing for anhidrosis does not depend on cooperation of the patient and can therefore be used in infants and children. Among the techniques recommended for mapping anhidrotic zones, the electric skin resistance test has found wider application (67) than the methods of visualizing sweating directly by means of indicators.

On anhidrotic skin areas the surface pH will no longer be influenced by sweat gland secretions, i.e., in most instances, by the acidic eccrine sweat, and the pH may be expected to rise. We have therefore determined the pH pattern in a number of children who had well-defined zones of anhidrosis due to various nerve injuries. It seems warrented to present the results of two such observations. We have had no opportunity yet to test the skin pH in anhidrosis due to congenital ectodermal dysplasia.

## Brachial Palsy

Among three subjects afflicted with this condition and tested for skin acidity was a female infant (No. 33–26–94) born with flaccid paralysis of the

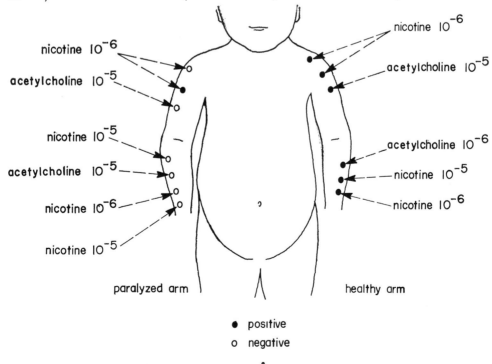

FIGURE 19. Sites and results of tests on the healthy and the paralyzed arm of a newborn infant with brachial palsy. A, intradermal sudorific tests on the volar aspects.

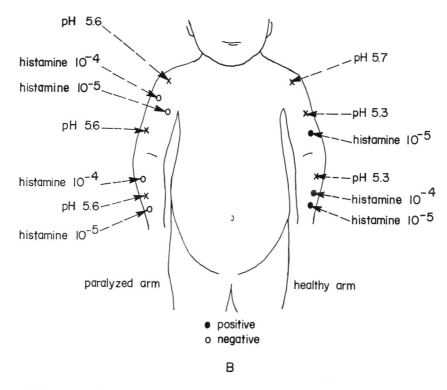

FIGURE 19 B. Same infant; intradermal *histamine* tests and skin *pH readings* on the volar aspects.

right upper and lower arm, with apparent absence of pain sensation in the affected extremity. Sweating ability on the involved arm was studied repeatedly during the first 3 weeks after birth. There was an anhidrotic zone extending distally onto the hand and proximally to a demarcation line in the acromial region. Within this zone, no thermal sweating could be visualized by the indicator methods of Wada (152) and Herrmann *et al.* (66), at a time when pronounced sweating could be demonstrated by the same methods on the healthy contralateral sites (at environmental temperatures of 30 to 32C). Furthermore, intradermal stimulation tests with acetylcholine and nicotine revealed that neither muscarinic sweating nor axon reflex sweating could be elicited on the anhidrotic paralyzed extremity, neither on flexor surfaces nor extensor surfaces.

The results of intradermal histamine tests suggested that the brachial palsy was of the postganglionic type (73): the axon reflex flare was missing in all but one of the reactions performed on the paralyzed arm, while normal triple responses were elicited in all tests performed on the healthy extremity.

The pH measurements with the glass electrode were similar on the paralyzed

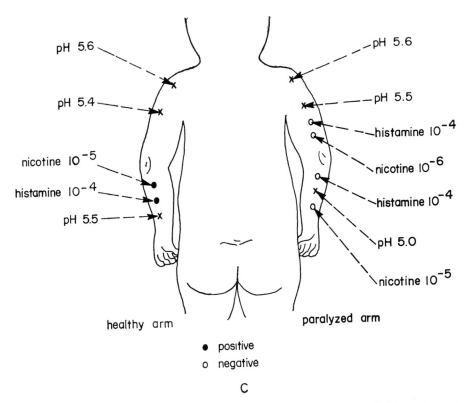

pH 5.6

pH 5.4

nicotine $10^{-5}$

histamine $10^{-4}$

pH 5.5

pH 5.6

pH 5.5

histamine $10^{-4}$

nicotine $10^{-6}$

histamine $10^{-4}$

pH 5.0

nicotine $10^{-5}$

healthy arm

paralyzed arm

● positive

○ negative

C

FIGURE 19 C. Same infant; intradermal *nicotine* and *histamine* tests and skin *pH readings* on the extensor aspects.

and healthy arm. Apparently, postganglionic nerve injury, though sufficiently extensive to sever sympathetic innervation of sweat glands, did not reduce surface acidity within the anhidrotic zone. Sites and results of the various tests are illustrated in Figure 19.

In a pertinent observation, Burckhardt (23) found normal alkali-resistance on the anhidrotic skin of a patient's paralyzed arm.

## Paraplegia

This study was carried out on a boy (No. ms63) with flaccid paralysis of both lower limbs, a paraplegia at level $T_{8-9}$. The condition was thought to be a transverse myelitis, secondary to thrombophlebitis (or abscess formation) which developed as a consequence of burns sustained at the age of 2 years and 7 months. The first- to second-degree burns had involved portions of both lower legs, genitalia, and perianal areas.

When we took up the evaluation of the autonomic functions in the paralyzed extremities, the patient was 4 years and 8 months old and had entered the hospital for one of his periodic examinations. In addition to the motor paralysis, there was complete sensory loss on both upper and lower legs and severe impairment of bladder and bowel function. The skin which had healed satisfactorily without requiring grafting was in good condition. Results of electromyographic studies were compatible with the diagnosis of complete lower neuron lesions in all affected muscles.

### Tests of Sweating Ability

At room temperature of 30 to 32C, the boy could be seen by indicator methods, to sweat spontaneously on forehead, chest, and upper extremities; no such thermal reflex sweating could be visualized on the paralyzed limbs. Within the anhidrotic zones, intradermal stimulation tests with adrenalin and acetylcholine were negative, indicating that the eccrine sweat glands were also unresponsive to direct-acting stimuli. Figure 20 shows the sites of drug injection, the outcome of each test, and the approximate demarcation

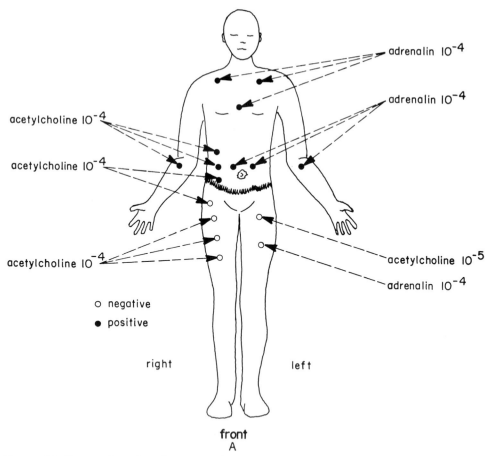

FIGURE 20. Sites and results of tests in a four and one-half year-old boy with paraplegia at T$_9$. A, intradermal sudorific tests.

line between surfaces with and without demonstrable thermal reflex sweating.

## Skin pH Measurements

Figure 20 illustrates the sites of potentiometric skin pH measurements and gives the obtained readings. All values are well within the physiologic range, but there is a slight difference between the main pH on anhidrotic and healthy skin, as the following tabulation shows:

| | Skin pH | | |
|---|---|---|---|
| | *Range* | *Mean* | *±SD* |
| above $T_9$ (left + right) | 4.7–6.0 | 5.31 | 0.30 |
| below $T_9$ (left + right) | 5.4–6.1 | 5.79 | 0.18 |
| on left half of body surface | 4.7–6.1 | 5.48 | 0.34 |
| on right half of body surface | 4.9–6.1 | 5.56 | 0.36 |

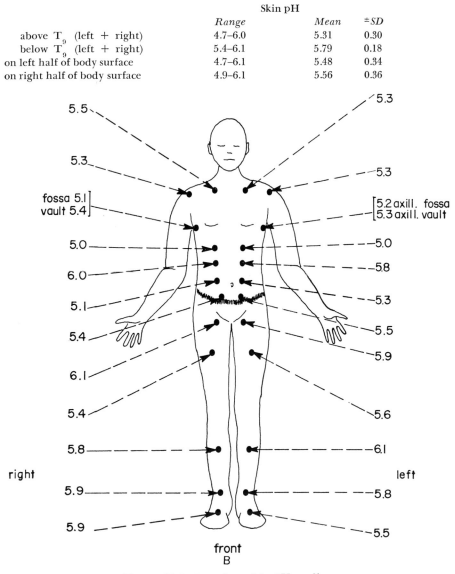

FIGURE 20 B. Same boy; skin *pH readings.*

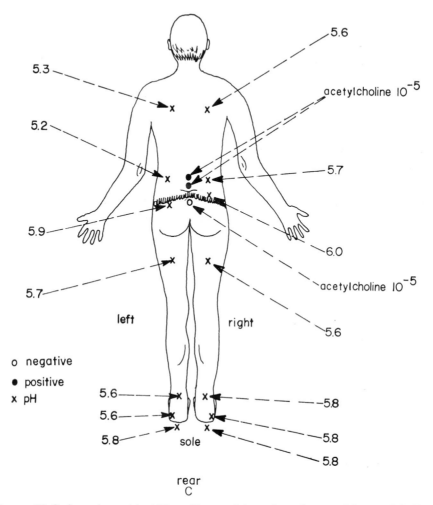

FIGURE 20 C. Same boy; skin *pH readings* and intradermal tests with *acetylcholine*.

Although there is a slight decline of skin acidity on the anhidrotic skin of the paralyzed part of the body, the nonsweating surfaces have retained a markedly acid pH. Figures for the left half and right half of the body surface are almost identical.

Thus, eccrine sweat can hardly be regarded as the primary source of surface acidification under the given conditions. These findings also suggest that skin pH determinations are not substitutes for the methods of sweat visualization in mapping the areas of anhidrosis, due to severance of sympathetic innervation.

## SURFACE pH AND HYPERHIDROSIS

Since electrolyte composition of sweat has been shown to vary with the rate of sweating (48,81) , hyperhidrosis could be expected to effect changes in surface pH. Investigating this possibility, Herrmann and Mandol (64) exposed healthy adults to dry heat (42C) for up to seventy minutes and determined the skin pH at various intervals at three sites, namely, temporal area, lateral upper back, and axillary vault. In male subjects, a slight rise or no elevation of the surface pH was found after an exposure for thirty minutes, while a distinct rise was noted in females. However, when thermal stimulation was extended to 60 minutes and sweating became more profuse, a gradual rise occurred in males, and a higher rise in females. The summary of results, shown in Table 30, indicates that the axillary pH does not participate in the response to heat (as tested in females) , and that the observed increases in pH are attributable to changes in eccrine sweat composition associated with the high rate of sweat delivery. This is evidenced directly by the documented similar pH increases in sweat samples collected from the two eccrine skin areas, increases which were not found in the axillary sweat.

TABLE 30
CHANGES IN SURFACE pH AFTER EXPOSURE OF THE BODY TO DRY HEAT
AT 42 C FOR SIXTY TO SEVENTY MINUTES*

|  | Mean Skin pH | |
|  | before | after |
|  | Exposure | |
| --- | --- | --- |
| Four Males | | |
| Temporal area | 4.9 | 6.5 |
| Back | 5.0 | 6.0 |
| Axill. vault | 7.3 | 7.4 |
| Two Females | | |
| Temporal area | 6.3 | 8.1 |
| Back | 5.9 | 8.5 |

*According to Herrmann and Mandol (64).

Since the same authors found increments in skin pH when sweating was induced by muscular exercise or sudorific drugs, they believe that there is a correlation of skin and sweat pH with the concentration of cholinergic agents at the effector organ.

In studies performed on 6-to 12-year-old boys, Emrich *et al.* (48) confirmed that the pH of eccrine sweat is a function of sweating rate. Their results indicate, further, the changes in lactic acid and carbon dioxide content of sweat with increasing rate of flow.

As pertinent to these studies, we would like to mention our findings in a 9-year-old girl (No. m223) with axillary hyperhidrosis. The patient had moderate amounts of pubic and axillary hair, modest development of breasts, but an infantile clitoris. She was suffering for some time from profuse secretion of foul-smelling sweat on both arm pits. Turbid, faintly greenish sweat could be seen dropping from both axillary spaces emitting a penetrating odor. The condition was thought of as axillary apocrine hyperhidrosis, possibly chromidrosis (128).

Potentiometric pH measurements showed the following values:

    on axillary vault,  7.4
    on axillary fossa,  6.2
    on shoulder        5.1

Thus, the outpouring sweat was obviously of apocrine nature, and the pH pattern normal for a girl who had just entered the last stage of sexual maturation. Apparently, the increased rate of apocrine sweat delivery did not produce a pH shift on the axillary vault (and in the apocrine sweat) beyond normal limits.

# Chapter X

# SKIN pH AND CONTACTANTS

Although skin defense against penetration from the outside is afforded in the main by the barrier membrane at the base of the horny layer, the surface film is also endowed with some protective capacities. Its acid pH per se serves in the defense against microorganisms. The very mechanism by which surface pH is homeostatically controlled, provides surface resistance against extraneous alkali and acids. The surface film participates in the defense against excessive removal of water and water-soluble substances.

## Alkali Resistance and Acid Resistance

The skin surface has the capacity to neutralize topically applied dilute acids and alkalies through the buffer systems described before. If the contacting substances are other than aqueous solutions, their physiochemical properties, in addition to their own buffering capacity, will interact with the surface's buffering power. This process of neutralization has been extensively studied in adults (23–26, 120, 121, 127) . Individuals can be differentiated into three groups with high, medium, or low buffering capacity, respectively. Subjects with low neutralizing ability are especially susceptible to the irritating effect of alkali, and predisposed to contract occupational eczema and dermatitis.

According to the procedures devised by Burckhardt (23) and Schuppli (124) , a drop of N/50 or N/100 NaOH or HCl solution, admixed with an indicator, is applied to the skin or to a piece of filter paper ($2 \times 3$ cm$^2$) placed on the skin. The time is noted when the pH has returned to the physiologic range of the acid mantle or to the value as determined at the same site prior to the test. In adults neutralization does not usually require more than thirty minutes, although there are wide individual variations. This procedure may be repeated several times at the same site. With each consecutive test, the buffering capacity declines and the neutralization time increases. Ultimately, the buffer reserves become exhausted and the pH of the test solution is no longer altered.

Follow-up of the pH changes is now carried out preferably with the glass electrode according to Schmid (120) , whose report gives further details on technic and evaluation.

Neutralization of topically applied ointments and creams can be studied with the electrode method only in oil-in-water emulsions; pH measurements in water-in-oil emulsions have to be made by means of the indicator method.

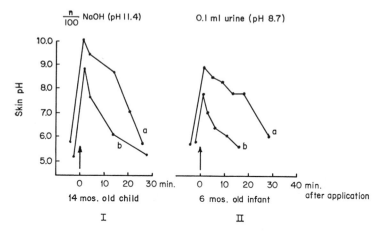

FIGURE 21. Alkali resistance of the skin surface in two children: *time curves of pH* reversal after application *(arrow)* of 0.1 ml (Ia) and 0.05 ml (Ib) of dilute alkali to the thigh; and of 0.1 ml of alkaline urine to lower leg (IIa) and to thigh (IIb).

Alkali-resistance should not be tested for in the presence of marked sweating, since the rate of sweat flow, when abnormally increased, shortens the neutralization time (112).

Judging from measurements we have made on young children, they are able to neutralize N/100 dilutions of NaOH with the same efficiency as adults. The example given in Figure 21 may suffice as evidence. It is not known yet, whether buffering capacity is already operative in the neonate's skin, or how soon after birth it becomes effective.

We have also measured pH changes on the intact surface resulting from topical application of creams of buffered aluminum acetate in a water-mis-

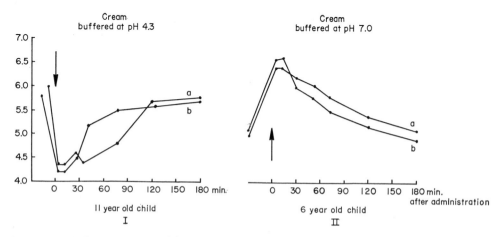

FIGURE 22. *Time curves of skin pH* reversal after topical application *(arrow)* of *creams buffered* at acid *pH (I)* and neutral *pH (II). a,* axillary vault; *b,* shoulder.

cible base;* the pH of the acid creams ranged from 4.3 to 4.7, that of the alkaline creams from 7.2 to 8.2. In children between 6 and 12 years of age it took from two to three hours until the pH on the anointed site had converted to the pH as read before the cream was applied. Two typical curves are reproduced in Figure 22. Neutralization takes place with the same efficiency as in similar tests in adults.

## Skin pH in Relation to Urinary and Fecal Diaper pH

### Influence of Urinary pH

That skin irritation in the diaper region is contingent upon an abnormally high pH of the contactant is not generally true. Rapp (110) has demonstrated that the production of erythema by dilute ammonia or ammonia-containing urine is indeed pH dependent, but the putrified urine, after removal of ammonia, still causes dermatitis, irrespective of the pH to which the test sample was adjusted.

One can easily demonstrate that ammoniacal urine applied to the skin is neutralized as effectively as dilute NaOH. An example of such a test (Figure 21) shows the topical pH changes on the thigh of a 6-month-old infant after application of 0.1 ml of putrified urine. The urine sample, collected from the infant on the preceding day and left to stand at room temperature, had a pH of 8.7 when used for the test.

To learn how skin pH is affected by prolonged contact with urine-soaked diapers, we have performed a series of tests in the following way: After removal of the wet diaper (containing no feces), the urinary pH was measured on the wet diaper with the glass electrode, and a first series of readings was obtained from seven sites within the skin region which had been covered by the diaper. Then the skin of the entire area was thoroughly washed with a water-soaked cloth for 2 minutes, dried superficially with gauze, and left exposed for 15 minutes. Thereafter, pH readings were repeated on all seven sites.**

The results obtained in 12 subjects are summarized in Table 31, which shows individual urinary pH values and mean skin pH readings for each child (i.e., subject means for all seven sites). In each of the first six subjects listed, the markedly acid urinary pH will be noted; and in all six children the subject means of surface pH on the uncleaned skin (column 2) hardly differs from the urinary pH values (column 1). The differences (column 4) average ±0.12.

In the last six subjects listed, who had a weakly acid or alkaline urinary pH,

---

* The creams were obtained from Dome Chemicals Inc. New York, through the courtesy of Bernard Idson, PhD.

** It would have been preferable in this and the subsequent study to measure the topical pH before and after contamination had taken place. Practical difficulties made this impossible.

TABLE 31
URINARY DIAPER pH AND SKIN pH BEFORE AND AFTER WASHING OF THE
CONTAMINATED AREAS. SUBJECT MEANS FROM SEVEN SITES FOR EACH
OF TWELVE CHILDREN BETWEEN THREE WEEKS AND TWO YEARS OF
AGE. POTENTIOMETRIC MEASUREMENTS

| Prot. No. | 1. Urinary Diaper pH | 2. Mean Skin pH Before Washing | 3. Mean Skin pH After Washing | 4. Differences 2.-1. | 5. Differences 3.-2. |
|---|---|---|---|---|---|
| J10 | 5.8 | 5.71 | 5.79 | −0.09 | +0.08 |
| J12 | 5.6 | 5.80 | 5.74 | +0.20 | −0.06 |
| J18 | 5.8 | 5.89 | 5.93 | +0.09 | +0.04 |
| J22 | 5.9 | 5.59 | 5.69 | −0.31 | +0.10 |
| J26 | 5.7 | 5.66 | 5.87 | −0.04 | +0.21 |
| J53 | 5.7 | 5.73 | 5.66 | +0.03 | −0.07 |
| J16 | 6.3 | 5.70 | 5.78 | −0.60 | +0.08 |
| J19 | 6.4 | 5.77 | 5.96 | −0.63 | +0.19 |
| J24 | 7.0 | 6.59 | 6.47 | −0.41 | −0.12 |
| J35 | 6.4 | 6.17 | 6.03 | −0.23 | −0.14 |
| J51 | 8.2 | 6.49 | 6.99 | −1.71 | +0.50 |
| J54 | 6.9 | 6.31 | 6.14 | −0.59 | −0.17 |
| 6 Infants | <6 | 5.73 | 5.78 | −0.12 | +0.05 |
| 6 Infants | >6 | 6.17 | 6.23 | −0.69 | +0.06 |

all subject means for uncleansed skin are markedly lower than the subjects' urinary pH, with an average difference of −0.69.

Apparently, no buffering action by the skin was called for during the contact with an acid urine (with a pH similar to that of the healthy skin). In contrast, contact with a neutral or alkaline urine induced defensive buffering action and resulted in a lowering of the pH, though not to physiologic levels.

Differences between cleansed and uncleansed skin are surprisingly small (column 5), regardless of the child's urinary pH, probably because the adhering contamination matter had lost its polarity.

TABLE 32
SURFACE pH ON URINE CONTAMINATED SKIN: SITE MEANS*

| SITE MEANS FOR 6 SUBJECTS DIAPER pH: 5.6-5.9 Before Washing Mean pH | S.D. | After Washing Mean pH | S.D. | Site | SITE MEANS FOR 6 SUBJECTS DIAPER pH: 6.3-8.2 Before Washing Mean pH | S.D. | After Washing Mean pH | S.D. |
|---|---|---|---|---|---|---|---|---|
| 5.81 | ±0.17 | 5.81 | ±0.17 | Abdomen, lower | 6.05 | ±0.33 | 6.33 | ±0.35 |
| 5.58 | 0.18 | 5.82 | 0.11 | Mons pubis | 6.45 | 0.59 | 6.47 | 0.64 |
| 5.92 | 0.23 | 5.95 | 0.26 | Inguinal fold, l. | 6.40 | 0.44 | 6.40 | 0.44 |
| 5.86 | 0.33 | 5.83 | 0.23 | Thigh, ant., left | 6.36 | 0.34 | 6.12 | 0.29 |
| 5.70 | 0.16 | 5.68 | 0.21 | Thigh, post, left | 6.22 | 0.54 | 6.18 | 0.33 |
| 5.88 | 0.16 | 5.83 | 0.14 | Buttocks, right | 6.17 | 0.39 | 6.32 | 0.42 |
| 5.60 | 0.33 | 5.68 | 0.28 | Coccygeal area | 5.63 | 0.40 | 5.92 | 0.41 |
| 5.74 | 0.27 | 5.80 | 0.23 | All 7 sites | 6.17 | 0.51 | 6.25 | 0.48 |

*Computed from the same pH readings as the subject means listed in Table 31.

Site means shown in Table 32 reveal the mean pH for each site to be higher in the six subjects with neutral or alkaline urine than in those with acid urine, even after washing. Once again it appears that the buffering power of the skin has been partly compromised upon exposure to urine of higher pH.

## Influence of Fecal pH

There can be little doubt that stools, especially if they are loose, have an irritant effect on the infant's skin. Whether this effect is pH dependent, remains as uncertain as the role of other factors in the production of diaper dermatitis (28). Pratt and Read (109) have measured the skin pH on perianal areas, first, while fecal matter adhered to the surface, and second, after the sites had been washed with water and dried with cotton sponges. Such tests were performed on 116 newborn infants on one of the first three days after birth, and on 135 infants at ages between 4 and 9 days.

In the younger age group the contaminated sites had a mean pH of 6.1 to 6.4, in the older group the means ranged from 5.7 to 6.2. After washing, the mean pH readings were only slightly lower. These findings provide little evidence with regard to the buffering capacity of the skin of the neonates, since fecal residues of markedly acid or alkaline reaction were obviously not encountered among the selected subjects. Most probably, fecal matter of an originally lower or higher pH had been already neutralized when readings were taken on the uncleansed skin. Inspite of these minor pH differences, the authors found a higher incidence of diaper dermatitis among infants with the higher fecal and perianal pH.

We have studied stool-induced pH changes on the skin of children accord-

TABLE 33

FECAL DIAPER pH AND SKIN pH BEFORE AND AFTER WASHING OF THE CONTAMINATED AREAS. SUBJECT MEANS FROM SEVEN SITES FOR EACH OF TEN CHILDREN BETWEEN TWO AND TWENTY MONTHS OF AGE POTENTIOMETRIC MEASUREMENTS

| Prot. No. | 1. Fecal diaper pH | 2. 3. Mean Skin pH | | 4. 5. Differences | |
|---|---|---|---|---|---|
| | | before | after | 2.-1. | 3.-2. |
| | | Washing | | | |
| J13 | 5.2 | 6.30 | 6.54 | +1.10 | +0.24 |
| J20 | 5.1 | 5.66 | 5.90 | +0.56 | +0.24 |
| J23 | 5.0 | 5.40 | 5.56 | +0.40 | +0.16 |
| J28 | 5.7 | 6.03 | 5.96 | +0.33 | −0.07 |
| J37 | 5.6 | 5.70 | 5.92 | +0.10 | +0.22 |
| J11 | 7.3 | 6.40 | 6.00 | −0.90 | −0.40 |
| J25 | 7.5 | 6.64 | 6.39 | −0.86 | −0.25 |
| J36 | 7.3 | 5.50 | 5.43 | −1.80 | +0.07 |
| J39 | 7.5 | 5.43 | 5.53 | −2.07 | −0.10 |
| J40 | 7.2 | 6.03 | 6.01 | −1.17 | +0.02 |
| 5 Infants | <6 | 5.82 | 5.98 | +0.50 | +0.16 |
| 5 Infants | >6 | 6.00 | 5.87 | −1.36 | −0.13 |

ing to the same procedure we applied in the tests with urine-wet diapers. Of the ten children tested, five had an acid fecal pH, the other five had an alkaline fecal diaper pH. The results are listed in Table 33 as subject means based on pH readings on seven sites. Most important is the difference between fecal pH (as measured in the diaper) and the mean skin pH as determined immediately after removal of the diaper, i.e., on the uncleansed skin. The dissimilarity of the changes in the skin pH as produced by contact with acid and alkaline stool, respectively, is striking (column 4). In all five cases with acid stools the mean pH on uncleansed skin is slightly higher than the stool pH; in the five infants with alkaline stools, the uncleansed skin pH is markedly lower than the fecal diaper pH, with an average difference of −1.36.

Differences between the subject means of skin pH for washed and nonwashed sites are as small as in the observations on urine contamination. In all cases but one, washing changed the pH by less than ±0.25 pH unit.

When the readings are computed as site means, as in Table 34, one can detect a trend of the prewashing values to exceed slightly the fecal diaper pH on most sites of the infants with the more acid stools. The opposite trend is discernable in the infants with more alkaline stools. The figures also indicate the insignificance of pH changes produced by washing.

TABLE 34
SURFACE pH ON STOOL CONTAMINATED SKIN: SITE MEANS*

| SITE MEANS FOR 5 SUBJECTS FECAL pH: 5.0-5.6 | | | | Site | SITE MEANS FOR 5 SUBJECTS FECAL pH: 7.2-7.5 | | | |
|---|---|---|---|---|---|---|---|---|
| Before Washing | | After Washing | | | Before Washing | | After Washing | |
| Mean pH | S.D. | Mean pH | S.D. | | Mean pH | S.D. | Mean pH | S.D. |
| 5.70 | ±0.35 | 6.13 | ±0.36 | Abdomen, lower | 5.98 | ±0.58 | 6.13 | ±0.40 |
| 5.70 | 0.40 | 6.15 | 0.43 | Mons pubis | 6.20 | 0.74 | 6.08 | 0.26 |
| 6.10 | 0.66 | 6.10 | 0.72 | Inguinal fold, l. | 6.15 | 0.72 | 6.08 | 0.49 |
| 5.68 | 0.29 | 5.86 | 0.33 | Thigh, anter., left | 5.93 | 0.39 | 5.83 | 0.38 |
| 6.08 | 0.78 | 6.12 | 0.66 | Thigh, post., left | 5.76 | 0.45 | 5.72 | 0.35 |
| 6.02 | 0.47 | 5.88 | 0.27 | Buttocks, right | 7.04 | 0.39 | 6.10 | 0.19 |
| 5.56 | 0.28 | 5.72 | 0.24 | Coccygeal area | 5.44 | 0.54 | 5.56 | 0.32 |
| 5.83 | 0.54 | 5.98 | 0.48 | All 7 sites | 6.07 | 0.74 | 5.91 | 0.40 |

*Computed from the same pH readings as the subject means listed in Table 33.

In summary, urinary and fecal residues, while in contact with the skin, undergo changes in pH which depend on the original reaction of the contaminant and the buffering capacity of the infant's skin. For urine with a pH of 6.3 to 8.2, the pH reduction is in the order of 0.4 to 1.7 units; for stools with a pH of 7.2 to 7.5 in the order of 0.9 to 2.0 units. Little buffer action is required when the urinary or fecal pH is between 5.1 and 5.9. Strongly acid urines or stools have not been tested. Washing off the residual urinary or fecal matter results in rather trifling changes in the surface pH. This was not anticipated since it is known that washing with water, if extended for 30 minutes, may cause a drop of skin pH by one unit (142). It may also be pertinent to note that ordinary hand washing with water for one minute, followed by drying for twenty seconds, reduces the surface lipids by an average of 25.3%, as found in adults (74).

## Skin pH in Relation to Skin Care

The efficacy of topical preparations will be enhanced, at least theoretically, if they act also to preserve or restore a normal skin pH. Properly buffered ointments and creams are not only widely preferred in the prophylaxis of skin lesions such as diaper dermatitis, but also as vehicles for specific pharmaca to be applied topically.

That the suitability of soaps, oils, and synthetic detergents as skin cleansers is also pH-dependent, has not yet been demonstrated convincingly. It should therefore, be of interest to mention here the results of two recently reported studies on changes in skin pH produced by the use of various types of cleansing preparations.

Posl and Schirren (108) examined the effect of soaps and soap substitutes on the skin pH of adults. In the first series of measurements, the products were applied only once to the skin for 30 minutes; in another series, the 30-minute contact was established three times a day for three consecutive days. Skin pH was measured potentiometrically before and after each exposure. In both series, the effect of soap and soap-like products with a pH of 9 to 10 was compared with that of synthetic detergents of which one group had a pH of 5 to 6.5, the other of 8.0.

The results indicate that the neutralizing capacity of the skin is not as heavily taxed by the detergents as by the soaps. Whether the cleanser was applied once or repeatedly to the same site, the rise in skin pH was higher (by about 2 units) after contact with alkaline soaps than with alkaline detergents (by about 1 unit). It appears that the differential pH of the cleansing agents explains these differences.

Similar studies were made by Pantlitschko *et al.* (104) on the effect of baby toiletries on the skin pH of healthy mature neonates. The products tested were white soap of pH 9.4, pHisoHex,® a hexachlorophene preparation of pH 5.5, and Pelsano,® an emulsion of triglyceride esters of linoleic and linolenic acid with a pH of 7.7.

After a single washing with white soap or pHisoHex, the authors found no significant shifts of skin pH during the subsequent 48 hours. However, a single washing with 0.25% Pelsano emulsion was followed by a marked decline of the skin pH in all skin areas tested. It is difficult to accept the authors' interpretation that the Pelsano bath alone has an acidifying effect and is therefore most suitable for the skin care of newborn infants. The data fail to show any relation between the pH of the various preparations and the direction or extent of the pH shift on the skin surface, a relation to be postulated if the pH changes were dependent on cutaneous buffering capacity. With or without participation of the skin's neutralizing mechanism, an acidifying effect of a product with a pH of 7.7 on the physiologically acid skin pH (4 to 6) is hard to conceive.

One will find less difficulty in interpreting the pH changes which the authors observed after washings performed several times daily for three consecutive days. Clearly, the alkalinizing effect of repeatedly applied soap could not be neutralized by the skin to the same degree as the effect of the less alkaline Pelsano emulsion. Readings taken on the soap-cleansed skin increased from day to day and reached levels which were by 0.5 to 1.0 pH unit higher than those attained on Pelsano-cleansed skin. The pH of the latter remained constant at a level of 6.5. Corresponding measurements after repeated use of the acid pHisoHex were not made. As the authors are aware, one has also to consider the physiologic decline of skin pH during the first postnatal week. However, there is no way in discerning the age factor in a study of this design.

# REFERENCES

1. Anderson, C. M., and Freeman, M.: "Sweat test" results in normal persons of different ages compared with families with fibrocystic disease of the pancreas. *Arch. Dis. Child., 35*:581, 1960.
2. Anderson, D. S.: Acid-base balance of the skin. *Brit. J. Derm., 63*:283, 1951.
3. Arbenz, H.: Untersuchungen über die pH-Werte der normalen Hautoberfläche. *Dermatologica, 105*:333, 1952.
4. Beare, J. M., Cheeseman, E. A., Gailey, A. A. H., and Neill, D. W.: The pH of the skin surface of children with seborrheic dermatitis compared with unaffected children. *Brit J. Derm., 70*:233, 1958.
5. Beare, J. M., Cheeseman, E. A., Gailey, A. A. H., Neill, D. W., and Merrett, J. D.: The pH of the skin surface of infants aged one to seven days. *Brit. J. Derm., 71*:165, 1959.
6. _____: The effect of age on the pH of the skin surface in the first week of life. *Ibid., 72*:62, 1960.
7. Becker, H.: Die Haut. In Brock, J. (Ed.): *Biologische Daten für den Kinderarzt, 2nd. ed.* Berlin, Springer, Vol. II, 1954, pp. 1042–1081.
8. Behrendt, H., and Green, M.: The relationship of skin pH pattern to sexual maturation of boys. *Amer. J. Dis. Child., 90*:164, 1955.
9. _____: Skin pH pattern in the newborn infant. *Ibid., 95*: 35, 1958.
10. _____: Skin pH pattern in relation to age and maturation. *Scientific Exhibit, International Congress of Pediatrics,* Lisbon, 1962, p. 59 (E57).
11. Behrendt, H., Green, M., and Carol, B.: Relation of skin pH pattern to sexual maturation in girls. *Amer. J. Dis. Child., 108*:37, 1964.
12. Bergeim, O., and Cornbleet, T.: The antibacterial action of the lactic acid and volatile fatty acids of sweat. *Amer. J. Med. Sci., 205*:785, 1943.
13. _____: Acidity of the scalp: nature and possible relation to seborrhea. *Arch. Derm. Syph., 56*:448, 1947.
14. Bernstein, E., and Herrmann, F.: The acidity on the skin surface. *New York J. Med., 42*:436, 1942.
15. Blank, I. H.: Measurement of the pH of the skin surface. I. Technique. *J. Invest. Derm., 2*:67, 1939.
16. _____ II. pH of exposed surfaces of adults with no apparent skin lesions. *Ibid., 2*:75, 1939.
17. _____ III. Measurements on the arms of children with no apparent skin lesions. *Ibid., 2*:231, 1939.
18. _____ IV. Daily variations for adult females with no apparent skin lesions. *Ibid., 2*:235, 1939.
19. Blank, I. H., and Coolidge, M. H.: Degerming cutaneous surface; quarternary ammonium compounds, *J. Invest. Derm., 15*:249, 1950.

20. Brown, H.: The mineral content of human skin. *J. Biol. Chem., 75*:789, 1927.
21. Brück, K.: Temperature regulation in the newborn infant. *Biol. Neonat., 3*:65, 1961.
22. Bunting, H., Wislocki, G. B., and Dempsey, E. W.: The chemical histology of human eccrine and apocrine sweat glands. *Anat. Rec., 100*:61, 1948.
23. Burckhardt, W.: Beitrage zur Ekzemfrage. II. Die Rolle des Alkali in der Pathogenese des Ekzems, speciel des Gewerbeekzems. *Arch. Derm. Syph., 173*:155, 1935.
24. _____ III. Die Rolle der Alkalischadigung der Haut bei der experimentellen Sensibilisierung gegen Nickel. *Ibid., 173*:262, 1935.
25. _____: Neuere Untersuchungen uber die Alkali-Empfindlichkeit der Haut. *Dermatologica, 94*:73, 1947.
26. Burckhardt, W., and Bäumle, W.: Die Beziehungen der Säureempfindlichkeit zur Alkaliempfindlichkeit der Haut. *Dermatologica, 102*:294, 1951.
27. Burckhardt, W., Locher, G., and Suter, H.: *Mechanismus der Entstehung der Hautreaktion gegenüber primartoxischen Substanzen. Rolle der Permeabilitat der Hornhaut. Proceedings of the XII International Congress of Dermatology.* Washington, D.C., 1962. Amsterdam, Excerpta Medica Foundation, 1963, Vol. I, p. 439.
28. Burgoon Jr., C., Urbach, F., and Grover, W.: Diaper dermatitis. *Pediat. Clin. N. Amer., 8*:835, 1961.
29. Buschke, W.: Cystenmamma und Axillarorgan. *Arch. Gynaek., 152*:431, 1933.
30. Clarke, J. T., Elian, E., and Shwachman, H.: Components of sweat. *Amer. J. Dis. Child., 101*:490, 1961.
31. Cmelik, S.: Ueber die unverseifbaren Lipoide der Vernix Caseosa. *Bioch. Z., 322*:355, 1952.
32. Cornbleet, T.: Self-sterilizing powers of the skin. V. Are they endowed by the surface acid? *Arch. Derm. Syph., 28*:526, 1933.
33. _____: Pregnancy and apocrine gland disease: Hidradenitis, Fox-Fordyce disease. *Ibid., 65*:12, 1952.
34. Cornbleet, T., and Meyer, E.: Sweat as a culture medium for fungi. *New Eng. J. Med., 230*:604, 1944.
35. Darling, R. C., and diSant' Agnese, P. A.: Electrolyte abnormalities of the sweat in fibrocystic disease of the pancreas. *Amer. J. Med. Sci., 225*:67, 1953.
36. Darrow, C. W.: Differences in psychological reactions to sensory and ideational stimuli. *Psychol. Bull., 26*:185, 1929.
37. Day, R.: Regulation of body temperature of premature infants. *Amer. J. Dis. Child., 65*:376, 1943.
38. DeBersaques, J., and Rothman, S.: Mechanism of keratin formation. *Nature, 193*:147, 1962.
39. Diczfalusy, E., and Lauritzen, C.: *Oestrogene beim Menschen.* Berlin, Heidelberg, Springer, 1961.
40. Dobszay, L.: Hormonal reactions of pregnancy. *Amer. J. Dis. Child., 56*:1280, 1938.

41. Downing, D. T., and Greene, R. S.: Double-bond positions in the unsaturated fatty acids of vernix caseosa. *J. Invest. Derm., 50*:380, 1968.

42. Draize, J. H.: Determination of pH of skin of man and common laboratory animals. *J. Invest. Derm., 5*:77, 1942.

43. Duncan, D. B.: Multiple range and multiple F tests. *Biometrics, 11*:1, 1955.

44. Ebling, F. J.: Sebaceous glands. I. The effect of sex hormones on the sebaceous glands of the female albino rat. *J. Endocr., 5*:297, 1948.

45. Eckstein, H. C.: The cholesterol content of hair, wool, and feathers. *J. Biol. Chem., 73*:363, 1927.

46. Ellis, R. A.: The fine structure of the eccrine sweat glands. *Advances Biol. Skin, 3*:30, 1962.

47. Emanuel, S.: Quantitative determinations of the sebaceous glands function, with particular mention of the method employed. *Acta. Dermatovener, 17*:444, 1936.

48. Emrich, H. M., Stoll, E., Friolet, B., Colombo, J. P., Richterich, R., and Rossi, E.: Sweat composition in relation to rate of sweating in patients with cystic fibrosis of the pancreas. *Pediat. Res., 2*:464, 1968.

49. Fraenkel, L., and Papanicolaou, G. N. Growth, desquamation, and involution of vaginal epithelium of fetuses and children, with consideration of related hormonal factors. *Amer. J. Anat., 62*:427, 1938.

50. Gans, B., and Thompson, J. C.: Neonatal oestrogen excretion and its relation to post-natal weight loss. *Proc. Roy. Soc. Med., 50*:929, 1957.

51. Gibson, L. E., and Cooke, R. E.: Test for concentration of electrolytes in sweat in cystic fibrosis of the pancreas utilizing pilocarpine by iontophoresis. *Pediatrics, 23*:545, 1959.

52. Gochberg, S. H., and Cooke, R. E.: Physiology of the sweat gland in cystic fibrosis of the pancreas. *Pediatrics, 18*:701, 1956.

53. Goldbloom, R. G., and Sekelj, P.: Cystic fibrosis of the pancreas. Diagnosis by application of a sodium electrode to the skin. *New Eng. J. Med., 269*:-1349, 1963.

54. Graef, H. J.: The endocrine influences on sebaceous glands. *Acta Brev. Neerland., 12*:67, 1942.

55. Green, M., Carol, B., and Behrendt, H.: Physiologic skin pH patterns in infants of low birth weight. *Amer. J. Dis. Child., 115*:9, 1968.

56. Greulich, W. W.: The relation of the developing apocrine sweat glands to the maturation of the reproductive system in children. *Anat. Rec.* (Suppl. 3), *67*:21, 1937.

57. Greulich, W. W., Dorman, R. I., Catchpole, H. R., Solomon, C. I., and Culotta, C. S.: Somatic and endocrine studies of puberal and adolescent boys. *Monogr. Soc. Res. Child Develop., 7*, (No. 3, Serial No. 33), Washington, Society for Research in Child Development, 1942.

58. Gronbaeck, P.: The sodium/potassium ratio in thermal sweat in patients with rheumatoid arthritis. *Acta Rheum. Scand., 6*:102, 1960.

59. Hamilton, J. B.: Male hormone substance: a prime factor in acne. *J. Clin. Endocr., 1*:570, 1941.

60. Harvey, W. R.: *Least-squares Analysis of Data with Unequal Subclass num-*

bers. Publication *ARS 20–8.* Agricultural Research Service, U. S. Dept. of Agriculture, April 1966.

61. Hashimoto, K., Gross, B. G., Di Bella, R. I., and Lever, W. F.: The ultrastructure of the skin of human embryos. IV. Epidermis. *J. Invest. Derm., 47*:317, 1966.

62. Herrmann, F., Behrendt, H., and Karp, F. L.: On the acidity of the surface of the scalp and other areas of the skin in children. *J. Invest. Derm., 7*:-215, 1946.

63. Herrmann, F., and Fuerst, K.: Ueber die Schweissekretion und ihre Bedeutung bei Dermatosen. *Derm. Wchr., 88*:397, 1929.

64. Herrmann, F., and Mandol, L.: Studies of pH of sweat produced by different forms of stimulation. *J. Invest. Derm., 24*:225, 1955.

65. Herrmann, F., and March, C.: Some physiological and clinical aspects of the water and electrolyte contents of the skin. *Med. Clin. N. Amer., 43*:635, 1959.

66. Herrmann, F., Prose, P. H., and Sulzberger, M. B.: Studies in sweating. IV. A new quantitative method of assaying sweat delivery to circumscribed areas of the skin surface. *J. Invest. Derm., 17*:241, 1951.

67. Herz, E., Glaser, G. H., Moldaver, J., and Hoen, T. I.: Electrical skin resistance test in evaluation of peripheral nerve injuries. *Arch Neurol. Psychiat., 56*:365, 1946.

68. Heuss, E.: Die Reaktion des Schweisses beim gesunden Menschen. *Monatsschr. f. prakt. Derm., 14*:343, 1892.

69. Hirsch, J.: *Fatty Acid Patterns in Human Adipose Tissue.* In Renold, A. E., and Cahill, G. F. (Eds.) : Adipose Tissue. *Handbook of Physiology,* Baltimore, Williams & Wilkins, 1965, Section 5, Chapter 17, pp. 181–190.

70. Hirsch, J., Farquhar, J. W., Ahrens, E. H., Peterson, M. L., and Stoffel, W.: Studies of adipose tissue in man. A microtechnic for sampling and analysis. *Amer. J. Clin. Nutr., 8*:499, 1960.

71. Hurley, H. J., and Shelley, W. B.: *The Human Apocrine Sweat Gland in Health and Disease.* Springfield, Ill., Thomas, 1960.

72. Hurst, R. L.: Analysis of variance and covariance: Unequal subclass frequences. *IBM, 1620, Users Group Library,* White Plains, New York, 6.0.132, 6–18.

73. Jost, F.: Die Beurteilung der Prognose der geburtstraumatischen Lähmung der oberen Extremität durch den Histamin Test. *Ann. Paediat., 202*:17, 1964.

74. Kirk, J. E.: Hand washing. *Acta dermatovener., 46, Suppl. 57,*1966.

75. Kligman, A. M., and Sheradeh, N.: Pubic apocrine glands and odor. *Arch. Derm., 89*:461, 1964.

76. Kooyman, D. J.: quoted from Rothman, S., (24i) .

77. Kuno, Y.: *Human Perspiration.* Springfield, Ill., Thomas, 1956. a) p. 123; b) p. 126; c) p. 151; d) p. 53.

78. Levin, O. L., and Silvers, S. H.: The reaction of the skin and its secretions in eczema. I. The hydrogen ion concentration of the skin surface in eczema. *Arch. Derm. Syph., 25*:825, 1932.

79. Lieberman, J., and Kellogg, F.: Evaluation of the sweat chloride assay in adults: Use of pilocarpine iontophoresis. *Amer. J. Med. Sci., 246*:537, 1963.

80. Lobeck, C. C., and Huebner, D.: Effect of age, sex and cystic fibrosis on the sodium and potassium content of human sweat. *Pediatrics, 30*:172, 1962.

81. Locke, W., Talbot, N. B., Jones, H. S., and Worcester, J.: Studies on the combined use of measurements of sweat electrolyte composition and rate of sweating as an index of adrenal cortical activity. *J. Clin. Invest., 30*:-325, 1951.

82. Lustig, B., and Perutz, A.: Ueber ein einfaches Verfahren zur Bestimmung der Wasserstoffionenkonzentration der normalen menschlichen Hautoberflaeche. *Arch. f. Derm. Syph., 162*:129, 1930.

83. Mali, J. W. H.: The transport of water through the human epidermis. *J. Invest. Derm., 27*:451, 1956.

84. Marchionini, A.: Untersuchungen uber die Wasserstoff-Ionen-Konzentration der Haut. *Arch. f. Derm. Syph., 158*:290, 1929.

85. _____: Zur Pathogenese und Differential-Diagnose dyshidrotischer und dyshidrosiformer Bläschenerkrankungen der Hände und Füsse. *Derm. Z., 58*:222, 1930.

86. Marchionini, A., Pascher, G., and Rockl, H.: Der pH-Wert der Hautoberfläche und seine Bedeutung im Rahmen der Bakterienabwehr. *Proceedings of the XII International Congress of Dermatology.* Washington, D. C., 1962. Amsterdam, Excerpta Medica Foundation, 1963, Vol. I, p. 396.

87. Marculli, F. N.: Barriers to skin penetration. *J. Invest. Derm., 39*:387, 1962.

88. Martner, J., Metcoff, J., and Antonowicz, I.: Chemical reorganization of human skin and skeletal muscle during growth. *Amer. J. Dis. Child., 93*:67, 1957.

89. Mattock, G.: The undressing of pH. *Lancet, 1*:803, 1962.

90. Mattock, G., and Band, D. M.: *Interpretation of pH and Cation Measurements.* In Eisenman, G. (Ed.). *Glass Electrodes for Hydrogen and other Cations.* New York, Marcel Dekker, 1967, p. 45.

91. Metcoff, J.: In Lanman, J. T. (Ed.) *Physiology of Prematurity. Transactions of the Fourth Conference,* Princeton, 1959. New York, Josiah Macy Jr. Foundation, 1960, pp. 125–126.

92. Meyer, A.: Vergleichende Gesamtsterin-und Sterinesterbestimmungen der Haut des wachsenden und erwachsenen Organismus. *Z. Kinderheilk., 50*:596, 1931.

93. Meyer, J. S., Gotoh, F., Tazaki, Y., and Hamaguchi, K.: Sodium and potassium activity of living brain. Relation to EEG and active sodium transport. *Trans. Amer. Neurol. Ass., 86*:17, 1961.

94. Montagna, W.: *The Structure and Function of the Skin,* 2nd ed. New York, Academic Press, 1962, a) p. 16–17; b) p. 273; c) p. 412.

95. _____: *The Epidermis. Proceedings of the XII. International Congress of Dermatology.* Washington, D.C., 1962. Amsterdam, Excerpta Medica Foundation, 1963, Vol. I, p. 359.

96. Montagna, W., Chase, H. B., and Hamilton, J. B.: The distribution of glycogen and lipids in human skin. *J. Invest. Derm., 17*:147, 1951.

97. Nathan, E., and Stern, F.: Ueber den Kalium-, Kalzium- und Wassergehalt der normalen Menschenhaut. *Derm. Z., 54*:14, 1928.

98. Nicolaides, N., Kellum, R. E., and Woolley, P. V.: The structures of the free unsaturated fatty acids of human skin surface lipid. *Arch Biochem., 105*:- 634, 1964.

99. Nicolaides, N., and Ray, T.: Skin lipids. III. Fatty chains in skin lipids. The use of vernix caseosa to differentiate between endogenous and exogenous components in human skin surface lipid. *J. Amer. Oil Chem. Soc., 42*:702, 1965.

100. Nicolaides, N. and Rothman, S.: Studies on the chemical composition of human hair fat. I. The squalene-cholesterol relationship in children and adults. *J. Invest. Derm., 19*:389, 1953.

101. O'Brien, D., Ibbott, F. A., and Rodgerson, D. O.: *Laboratory Manual of Pediatric Micro-Biochemical Techniques.* 4th ed. New York, Harper, 1968, p. 16.

102. Onken, M. D., and Moyer, C. A.: The water barrier in human epidermis. *J. Invest. Derm., 87*:584, 1963.

103. Pana, C.: Recerche sulla variazioni strutturali delle ghiandole apocrine as- cellari in relazione allo delle ghiandole sessuali e della mammella. *Speri- mentale, 88*:580, 1934.

104. Pantlitschko, M., Widhalm, S., and Zweymüller, E.: Einfluss der Pflege auf das Haut-pH des gesunden reifen Neugeborenen. *Wien. klin. Wschr., 78*:665, 1966.

105. Peck, S. M., and Rosenfeld, H.: The effects of hydrogen ion concentration, fatty acids and vitamin C on the growth of fungi. *J. Invest. Derm., 1*:237, 1938.

106. Pietrzykowa, A.: Some function tests in senile skin. *Przegl. Derm., 52*:581, 1965.

107. Pillsbury, D. M., and Rebell, G. C.: Bacterial flora of skin; factors influenc- ing growth of resident and transient organisms. *J. Invest. Derm., 18*:173, 1952.

108. Pösl, H., and Schirren, C. G.: Beeinflussung des pH-Wertes der Hautober- fläche durch Seifen, Waschmittel, und synthetische Detergentien. *Haut- arzt, 17*:37, 1966.

109. Pratt, A. G., and Read, W. T.: Influence of type of feeding on pH of stool, pH of urine, and incidence of perianal dermatitis in the newborn infant. *J. Pediat., 46*:539, 1955.

110. Rapp, G. W.: The etiology of urine diaper rash. *Arch. Ped., 72*:113, 1955.

111. Richter, W.: Beiträge zur normalen und pathologischen Anatomie der apo- krinen Hautdrüsen des Menschen, mit besonderer Berücksichtigung des Achselhöhlenorgans. *Virchow's Arch f. Path. Anat., 287*:277, 1932.

112. Robert, P., and Jaddou, J.: Untersuchungen über den Einfluss der Schweis- sekretion auf die Alkalineutralisationsfähigkeit der Haut. *Dermatologica, 86*:72, 1942.

113. Rony, H. R., and Zakon, S. J.: Effect of androgen on the sebaceous glands of human skin. *Arch. Derm. Syph., 48*:601, 1943.

114. Rothberg, S.: *Chemistry of Pathological Keratinization. Proceedings of the XII. International Congress of Dermatology,* Washington, D.C., 1962. Amsterdam, Excerpta Medica Foundation, 1963, Vol. I, p. 423.

115. _____: The synthesis of epidermal proteins. I. Alkali solubilized (insoluble) proteins. *J. Invest. Derm., 43*:151, 1965.

116. Rothman, S.: *Physiology and Biochemistry of the Skin.* Chicago, Univ. of Chicago Press, 1954, a) pp. 183–186; b) p. 191; c) pp. 201–216; d) p. 222; e) p. 285; f) pp. 295–296; g) p. 340; h) p. 368.

117. Rothman S., and Lorincz, A. L.: Defense mechanism of the skin. *Ann. Rev. Med., 14*:215, 1963.

118. Schade, H., and Marchionini, A.: Der Säuremantel der Haut (nach Gasketenmessungen). *Klin. Wschr., 7*:12, 1928.

119. Schiefferdecker, P.: *Die Hautdrüsen des Menschen und der Säugetiere, ihre Biologische und Rassenanatomische Bedeutung, sowie die muscularis sexualis.* Stuttgart, Schweitzerbarthsche Verlagsbuchhandlung, 1922.

120. Schmid, M.: Vergleichende Untersuchungen über die Säure-Basenverhältnisse auf der Haut. *Dermatologica, 104*:367, 1952.

121. Schmidt, P. W.: Ueber die Beeinflussung der Wasserstoffionen-Konzentration der Hautoberfläche durch Säuren. Betrachtungen über die Funktionen des "Säuremantels". *Arch. f. Derm. Syph., 182*:102, 1941.

122. Schonfeld, W. A.: Primary and secondary sexual characteristics: Study of their development in males from birth through maturity, with biometric study of penis and testes. *Amer. J. Dis. Child., 65*:535, 1943.

123. _____: General practitioner's role in management of personality problems of adolescents. *J. A. M. A., 147*:1424, 1951.

124. Schuppli, R.: Untersuchungen über das Säure-Neutralizations-vermögen der Haut. *Dermatologica, 98*:295, 1949.

125. Sekelj, P., and Goldbloom, R. B.: *Clinical Application of Cation-Sensitive Glass Electrodes.* In Eisenman, G. (Ed.) : *Glass Electrodes for Hydrogen and other Cations.* New York, Marcel Dekker, 1967, Chapter 19, p. 520.

126. Serri, F., and Montagna, W.: The structure and function of the epidermis. *Pediat. Clin. N. Amer., 8*:917, 1961.

127. Sharlit, H., and Scheer, M.: The hydrogen ion concentration of the surface on the healthy intact skin. *Arch. Derm. Syph., 7*:592, 1923.

128. Shelley, W. B., and Hurley, H. J.: Localized chromidrosis: Disorder of the apocrine gland. *J. Invest. Derm., 19*:265, 1952.

129. _____: The physiology of the human axillary apocrine sweat gland. *J. Invest. Derm., 20*:285, 1953.

130. Spier, H. W., and Pascher, G.: Quantitative Untersuchungen über die freien Aminosäuren der Hautoberfläche. Zur Frage ihrer Genese. *Klin. Wschr., 11*:997, 1953.

131. _____: Zur analytischen und funktionellen Physiologie der Hautoberfläche. *Hautarzt, 7*:55, 1956.

132. Spier, H. W., and Schwarz, E: *Chemie der Hornschicht. Proceedings of the*

*XII. International Congress of Dermatology,* Washington, D.C., 1962. Amsterdam, Excerpta Medica Foundation, 1963, Vol. I, p. 389.

133. Spier, H. W., Szakall, A., Fisher, A., and Klaschka, F.: Skin stress, its features and sequelae. *Derm. Wschr., 142*:1073, 1960.

134. Strauss, J. S., Kligman, A. M., and Pochi, P. E.: The effect of androgens and estrogens on human sebaceous glands. *J. Invest. Derm., 39*:135, 1962.

135. Stuart, H. C., and Sobel, E. H.: The thickness of the skin and subcutaneous tissue by age and sex in childhood. *J. Pediat., 28*:637, 1946.

136. Stur, O.: Die Elektrolytkonzentrationen im Schweiss von Neugeborenen. Neue Oesterr. *Z. Kinderheilk, 6*:347, 1961.

137. Sulzberger, M. B., and Herrmann, F.: Some new observations on the biology of the skin surface. *Arch Derm., 81*:235, 1960.

138. Swanbeck, G.: Macromolecular organization of epidermal keratin; an X-ray diffraction study of the horny layer from normal, ichthyotic and psoriatic skin. *Acta Dermatovener. 39, Suppl.* 43, 1959.

139. Sweeney, M. J., Etteldorf, J. N., Throop, L. J., Timma, D. L., and Wrenn, E. L.: Diet and fatty acid distribution in subcutaneous fat and in the cholesterol-triglyceride fraction of serum of young infants. *J. Clin. Invest., 42*:1, 1963.

140. Szabo, G.: The number of sweat glands in human skin. *Advances in Biology of Skin, 3*:3, 1962.

141. Szakall, A.: Ueber die Physiologie der obersten Hautschichten und ihre Bedeutung für die Alkaliresistenz. *Arbeitsphysiol., 11*:436, 1941.

142. _____: Die Veränderungen der obersten Hautschichten durch den Dauergebrauch einiger Handwaschmittel. *Ibid., 13*:49, 1943.

143. _____: Ueber die Eigenschaften, Herkunft und physiologischen Funktionen der die H-ionenkonzentration bestimmenden Wirkstoffe in der verhornten Epidermis. *Arch. Klin. Exp. Derm., 201*:331, 1955.

144. _____: The Epidermal Barrier. *Proceedings of the XII. International Congress of Dermatology,* Washington, D.C., 1962. Amsterdam, Excerpta Medica Foundation, 1963, Vol. I, p. 404.

145. Taddei, A.: Ricerche, mediante indicatori, sulla reazione attuale della cute nel neonato. *Riv. Ital. Ginec., 18*:496, 1935.

146. Talbot, N. B., Sobel, E. H., McArthur, J. W., and Crawford, J. D.: *Functional Endocrinology from Birth through Adolescence.* Cambridge, Mass., Harvard Univ. Press, 1952, Chapter V, pp. 299–317.

147. Thomas, E.: *Drüsen Mit Innerer Sekretion.* In Brock, J. (Ed.): *Biologische Daten Für Den Kinderarzt,* 2nd ed., Berlin, Springer, Vol. II, 1954, pp. 585–586.

148. Thurmon, F. M., and Ottenstein, G.: Studies on the chemistry of human perspiration with especial reference to its lactic acid content. *J. Invest. Derm., 18*:333, 1952.

149. Tomicek, O.: *Chemical Indicators.* London, Butterworth, 1951.

150. Unna, P. G., and Godolitz, L.: Zur Chemie der Haut. *Monatsschr. f. Prakt. Derm., 50*:451, 1910.

151. Vinnic, C. A., and Grann, V. R.: Attempted cultivation of spirochaeta myelophtora and a test of the validity of the complement-fixation test in multiple sclerosis. *New Eng., J. Med., 266*:1084, 1962.

152. Wada, M.: Sudorific action of adrenalin on the human sweat glands and determination of their excitability. *Science, 111*:376, 1950.

153. Waelsch, L.: Ueber Veränderungen der Achselschweissdrüsen während der Gravidität. *Arch. f. Derm. Syph., 114*:139, 1913.

154. Warwick, W. J., and Hansen, L.: The silver electrode method for the rapid analysis of sweat chloride. *Pediatrics, 36*:261, 1965.

155. Weitkamp, A. W., Smiljanik, A. M., and Rothman, S.: The free fatty acids of human hair fat. *J. Amer. Chem. Soc., 69*:1936, 1947.

156. Widdowson, E. M.: Chemical structure, functional integration, and renal regulation as factors in the physiology of the newborn. In Lanman, J. T. (Ed.) : *Physiology of Prematurity. Transactions of the Fourth Conference,* Princeton, N. J., 1959. New York, Josiah Macy Jr. Foundation, 1960, pp. 97–114.

157. Widdowson, E. M., and Dickerson, J. W. T.: The effect of growth and function on the chemical composition of soft tissues. *Biochem. J., 77*:30, 1960.

158. Wilkerson, V. A.: Chemistry of human epidermis; amino acid content of stratum corneum and its comparison to other human keratins. *J. Biol. Chem., 107*:377, 1934.

# INDEX